はしがき

　物事を成就させるためには、その過程こそが大切です。『seek next 英語総合問題 SECOND EDITION』シリーズは、日頃の基礎固めの英語学習から、さらに受験に対応する力までを養成するために編集された総合問題集です。当シリーズは、各学習段階に応じた5冊から成り、「文法」「作文」「リスニング」「速読」「長文読解」を中心とした構成となっています。

　このシリーズの3冊目にあたる本書『seek next 3 SECOND EDITION』は、文法体系に基づく展開で、各レッスンの文法事項を軸として学習を進められるようにしています。各レッスンの「文法」の文法事項が「作文」「長文読解」へと連動しており、文法事項を確実に定着できるように工夫しています。

　また、各レッスンの「リスニング」と「速読」では、「長文読解」と同じテーマや、関連したテーマの英文を収録しています。リスニングや掲示、パンフレット、広告などのさまざまな読み物を通して、「長文読解」の題材に関する知識を深めることができるようにしてい

JN102707

本書の構成と特色

各レッスンは4ページ構成で、全部で15レッスンから成っています。各レッスンを「文法」➡「作文」➡「リスニング」➡「速読」➡「長文読解」の流れで構成しました。

■ Grammar
●必ず習得するべき重要項目を厳選し、文法体系に基づいて15レッスンに配しました。

■ Writing
●各レッスンの文法事項をふまえた部分整序作文問題もしくは英訳完成問題です。Grammar と連動した問題内容です。

■ Listening
●各レッスンの「長文読解」と同じテーマの英文を聞き取ります。
●さまざまな試験の形式に対応した問題を収録しています。
●(🔊) は、教師用付属の音声 CD のトラック番号を示します。二次元コードを読み取って、音声を PC やスマートフォンなどから聞くこともできます。

■ Rapid Reading
●各レッスンの「長文読解」と同じテーマの英文を収録しています。
●ふつうの英文だけでなく、掲示、広告、メールなどの読み取り問題など、さまざまな形式の問題を収録しています。

■ Reading
●各レッスンの文法事項を含んだ長文読解問題です。興味を引く題材、知的好奇心を喚起する題材、SDGs に対応した題材を選びました。
●各レッスンの「リスニング」と「速読」と同じテーマの英文を収録しています。
●速読問題：設定された時間内に本文を読み、本文の要旨や概要についての理解を問う問題としました。
●精読問題：本文の内容上の重要箇所に関する問題や文法事項を含む問題、本文全体に関する内容把握問題から成ります。

CAN-DO List
●各レッスンの学習の到達目標を「知識・技能」、「思考力・判断力・表現力」の観点から示しています。満点が取れたら、□にチェックを入れましょう。

Contents

Rapid Reading		Reading		
テーマ	問題形式			
IT	GTEC®	スティーブ・ジョブズについて。		260 words
ニュース	共通テスト	パーソナライズされたニュースについて。	16 PEACE, JUSTICE AND STRONG INSTITUTIONS	246 words
気候変動	英検®	気候変動について。	13 CLIMATE ACTION	259 words
コミュニケーション		ほめ言葉について。		294 words
インフラ		インフラの補修について。	9 INDUSTRY, INNOVATION AND INFRASTRUCTURE 11 SUSTAINABLE CITIES AND COMMUNITIES	322 words
昆虫	英検®	クモについて。		307 words
スケジュール	英検®	時間管理について。	8 DECENT WORK AND ECONOMIC GROWTH	312 words
標識	GTEC®	休暇でのできごと。		304 words
自然	GTEC®	イエローストーン国立公園の大火災について。	15 LIFE ON LAND	322 words
職業		就職活動に成功するために。	8 DECENT WORK AND ECONOMIC GROWTH	335 words
漫画	英検®	チャールズ・シュルツが漫画家になるまで。		340 words
自然	英検®	虹について。		318 words
教育	英検®	平等な教育とは。	4 QUALITY EDUCATION	328 words
道案内	英検®	地域によって異なる人々の性格。		322 words
フードマイル		フードマイルについて。	12 RESPONSIBLE CONSUMPTION AND PRODUCTION 13 CLIMATE ACTION	358 words

Lesson 1 文型

Grammar 目標➡7分

1 次の各文の（　　）内に下記の語群から適語を選んで補いなさい。ただし、文頭にくるべき語も小文字で示しています。 (各2点)

1. Many people in our town （　　　　　　　　） in the local factory.
2. You will （　　　　　　　） better after a night's sleep.
3. （　　　　　　　　） the dog a bone, and that should （　　　　　　　） him quiet.
4. Glasses （　　　　　　　） our appearance.　Some people refuse to wear glasses because they think they （　　　　　　） better without them.

【change / feel / give / keep / look / work】

2 次の各文の（　　）内に入れるのに最も適当なものを選び、記号を補いなさい。 (各2点)

1. She switched off the light and （　　　） on the bed.
   　a. lay 　　　　　　b. laid 　　　　　　c. lain 　　　　　　d. lied
2. The two friends （　　　） their summer vacations.
   　a. discussed 　　　b. discussed about 　c. discussed of 　　d. discussed on
3. A police officer （　　　） her hand to stop traffic.
   　a. arose 　　　　　b. got up 　　　　　c. raised 　　　　　d. rose
4. I can't （　　　） you how pleased I am to hear your good news.
   　a. say 　　　　　　b. speak 　　　　　　c. tell 　　　　　　d. talk

Writing 目標➡5分

3 （　　）内に与えられた語句を並べかえて、英文を完成しなさい。 (各4点)

1. 暑い日には涼しいそよ風は心地いいですね。
   A cool breeze (a hot day / feels / good / on), doesn't it?

2. 彼は、工場が閉鎖されて失業した。
   He (closed / his job / lost / the factory / when).

3. この券があれば私たちの会社のバスにあなたは無料で乗れます。
   This ticket (gives / the right / to / travel / you) free on our buses.

4. 彼は幽霊を信じているので暗やみをこわがるのです。
   His belief in ghosts (afraid / him / makes / of / the dark).

4 それぞれの写真について 4 つの説明が読まれます。写真に最も合っているものを一つずつ選びなさい。 (各5点)

1.

① ② ③ ④

2.

① ② ③ ④

Rapid Reading 目標➡ 5分   テーマ IT GTEC®

5 広告を読み取って、問いに対する答えとして最も適当なものを一つずつ選びなさい。 (各5点)

VENUS LAPTOP COMPUTER
～JAPAN ELECTRIC SHOP～

New Product

Venus Laptop Computer is designed to balance mobility and productivity for everyone. It adopts cutting-edge technology and has a compact body. It is ultralight and features a battery that lasts a full work day. So, it is much easier to carry and allows you to work the way you want.

Price

・We limit its price to 200,000 yen.

・We offer a 10% student discount as the deal of this month.

・If you show your student ID card to the store, we will give you a 10% discount off the price tag. Don't miss this chance!

JAPAN ELECTRIC SHOP
URL : www.japanelectricshop.com
TEL : (0120) 37-XXXX

---

1. According to the advertisement, how often do we have to charge the battery in a day?
   ① Only once before using.
   ② Once while using.
   ③ Twice.
   ④ Depends on the usage.

2. Taro, a university student, got a Venus Laptop Computer last month. How much did he pay for it?
   ① 160,000 yen.　② 180,000 yen.　③ 200,000 yen.　④ 220,000 yen.

速 読問題 次の英文を2.5分で読んで、1. の問いに答えなさい。

In December 1980, *Apple's *shares were listed on the New York stock market.   Although Jobs was only 25 years old, his stock was worth over $250 million.   Handsome young Steve Jobs became the symbol of a new breed of *Silicon Valley (1)entrepreneur.

Jef Raskin, an engineer at Apple, was (2)in charge of a project called Macintosh.   His plan

5 was to create a cheap $1,000 computer for ordinary people.

After losing the *Lisa project, Jobs was looking for something to do.   (3)He pushed Raskin out and took over the Macintosh project.   He increased the number of engineers on the team. Jobs didn't care if the computer was cheap or profitable.   He wanted it to be "great."

First of all, he wanted it to be small.   The bottom of the computer should be no bigger than

10 a telephone book, he told his staff.   Because he wanted the text display to be attractive, he got a high school friend to develop all sorts of new *fonts for the computer.   Jobs also wanted the Macintosh to have an attractive case.   To find a good designer, he organized a design contest. The winner was Hartmut Esslinger, a German who had designed Sony's Trinitron televisions.

Jobs liked German design.   He loved Porsche and Mercedes cars, and he was a big fan of

15 Dieter Rams, the German industrial designer who designed electronic devices for *Braun. Jobs, like Rams, believed that simple, easy-to-understand design was best.   For the Macintosh, Jobs wanted Esslinger to create a white, "high-tech" look, the opposite of the heavy, black, "industrial" look of Sony.

(260 words)

---

1 Apple：アップル(スティーブ・ジョブズの創立した会社)　　1 share[ʃéər]：株式(＝stock)
3 Silicon Valley：シリコンバレー(サンフランシスコ郊外のエレクトロニクス産業の集まった地域)
6 Lisa：1983年にアップルが製造したコンピュータ　　11 font[fá(:)nt]：(活字の)書体
15 Braun：ドイツの小型電気器具メーカー

1. この英文のタイトルとして最も適当なものを、次の a.～ d. から選びなさい。　　　　（5点）

　　a．アップル社の株式上場

　　b．ジェフ・ラスキンの活躍

　　c．スティーブ・ジョブズのドイツ製品へのあこがれ

　　d．マッキントッシュの誕生

精 読問題 もう一度英文を読んで、次の問いに答えなさい。

2. 下線部(1)の意味として最も適当なものを a.～ d. から一つ選びなさい。　　　　（3点）

　　a．a person who does something first and so makes it possible or easier for others to do it later

　　b．a person who has a million dollars; a very rich person

　　c．a person who starts a company and makes business risks in the hope of making a profit

　　d．an owner of shares in a business

3. 下線部(2)の意味として最も適当なものを a.～ d. から一つ選びなさい。　　　　（5点）

　　a．in opposition to 　　　　　　　　　　 b．in relation to

　　c．in favor of 　　　　　　　　　　　　　 d．responsible for

4. 文法 下線部(3)について、ラスキンとジョブズはそれぞれマッキントッシュをどのようなコンピュータにしたいと考えていましたか。第2・3パラグラフからそれを的確に表す形容詞を抜き出しなさい。　　　　（各5点）

　　ラスキン：＿＿＿＿＿＿＿＿＿＿＿＿　　　　ジョブズ：＿＿＿＿＿＿＿＿＿＿＿＿

5. ジョブズが追求したマッキントッシュの鍵となる形容詞を、第4パラグラフから二つ抜き出しなさい。　　　　（各6点）

　　＿＿＿＿＿＿＿＿＿＿＿＿　　　＿＿＿＿＿＿＿＿＿＿＿＿

6. ジョブズとラムスのデザインに対する共通した考え方を表す箇所を、本文中から抜き出しなさい。

　　　　（8点）

7. 全体把握 本文の内容と合っているものにはT、合っていないものにはFと答えなさい。 （各1点）

　　(ア) Steve Jobs became the symbolic figure of the new generation of Silicon Valley when he was 25. 　　　　　　　　　　　　　　　　　　　　　　　　　　（　　）

　　(イ) The Lisa project was successful. 　　　　　　　　　　　　　　　（　　）

　　(ウ) Steve Jobs thought that the price of his computer was important. 　　（　　）

　　(エ) Steve Jobs told his staff to make his computer as big as possible. 　　（　　）

　　(オ) Dieter Rams was Steve Jobs' favorite industrial designer. 　　　　（　　）

Lesson 2 時制①

Grammar 目標➡7分

1 次の各文の(　)内から適当なほうを選びなさい。 (各2点)

1. What time (are you meeting / do you meet) Ann tomorrow?

2. The plane (arrives / is arriving) in New York at 7:30 tomorrow morning.

3. We (go / are going) to a concert tonight.　It (is starting / starts) at 7:30.

4. Don't call me between 7:00 and 8:00.　We (will be having / will have had) dinner then.

5. Call me after 8:00.　We (will be finishing / will have finished) dinner by then.

2 次の各文の[　]内の動詞を適当な形にして(　)内に補いなさい。 (各2点)

1. If Tom (　　　　　　　　) the examination, his father is going to buy him a bicycle.

[pass]

2. Please put the book back on the shelf when you (　　　　　　) (　　　　　　) it.

[read]

3. Don't talk to him now—wait till his anger (　　　　　　) down.　[die]

4. Let's go for a walk as soon as it (　　　　　　) raining.　[stop]

Writing 目標➡3分

3 (　)内に適語を補って、英文を完成しなさい。 (各3点)

1. 私たちは明日出発します。ビルが空港で見送ってくれることになっています。

We're (　　　　　　　　) tomorrow.　Bill is (　　　　　　　　) us off at the airport.

2. すみません。この電車はニューヨークに何時に着くのですか。

Excuse me.　What time (　　　　　　　　) this train (　　　　　　　　) to New York?

3. 来週の今頃は、私は浜辺で寝そべっているか、海で泳いでいることでしょう。

This time next week I'll be (　　　　　　　　) on a beach or (　　　　　　　　) in the sea.

4. 明日で、ジーンとケンが結婚して10年になります。

Tomorrow Jean and Ken will have (　　　　　　　) (　　　　　　　) for ten years.

5. この薬を飲めば、気分がよくなるでしょうよ。

If you (　　　　　　　) this medicine, you will (　　　　　　　) better.

6. 大きくなったら何になりたいの?

What do you want to do (　　　　　　　) you (　　　　　　　) up?

7. 準備ができたらすぐに私は出発します。

I'll leave as (　　　　　　) as I (　　　　　　) ready.

CAN-DO List □ 🔍 〈知識・技能〉未来を表す表現、時や条件を表す副詞節を適切に活用することができる。

Listening

目標➡5分　　　　　テーマ ニュース　英検®　 5〜6

4 対話を聞き、最後の発言に対する相手の応答として最も適当なものを一つずつ選びなさい。

1. ① My English teacher knows about good news.　　　　　　　(各5点)
   ② Oh, I didn't know about that!
   ③ You are talking about the four directions.
   ④ You can read a lot of news online.

2. ① Learning English is always a lot of fun.
   ② It's called World English News.
   ③ It's so popular among English learners.
   ④ The name has already been decided.

Rapid Reading

目標➡5分　　　　　テーマ ニュース　共通テスト

5 社説を読み取って、問いに対する答えとして最も適当なものを一つずつ選びなさい。　(各5点)

Student Editorial Contest

This editorial is by one of the Top Ten Winners

Shu Uemura, age 18

The streets of Osaka have become filled with so many delivery drivers.　They deliver pizzas, hamburgers, noodles, or even sushi.　The demand for food delivery is increasing day by day.　Now, in Japan, more than 100,000 people work as a food delivery driver.　More people are starting to work as delivery drivers.　More and more restaurants are making contracts with delivery companies in Japan.

While a lot of consumers think this service is convenient, we are still not aware of the problems caused by this changing situation.　According to a survey, nearly one third of the delivery drivers in Osaka work more than 12 hours a day, especially on rainy days.　This means that delivery companies need more drivers in order to keep the delivery service going. We should pay more attention to who really offers us this convenient service : the food delivery drivers.　It would be a good idea to show more respect for them.

---

1. One fact from the article is that ☐ .
   ① more and more restaurants are employing delivery drivers
   ② so many bicycle riders have started to work for restaurants
   ③ the number of delivery companies in Japan is decreasing
   ④ the number of food delivery drivers is increasing

2. One opinion from the article is that ☐ .
   ① nearly one third of the delivery drivers in Japan work longer hours than average workers
   ② we already know well about the problems caused by delivery companies
   ③ we should look up to food delivery drivers
   ④ we should pay more attention to restaurants in Japan

　□ 🎧 〈思考力・判断力・表現力〉短い対話を聞いて、内容を理解できる。

□ 💬 〈思考力・判断力・表現力〉社説から、情報を事実と意見に整理することができる。　　**Lesson 2** | 9

Reading 目標➡20分 文法項目 時や条件を表す副詞節 テーマ ニュース 🔊 7

速 **読問題** 次の英文を2.5分で読んで、1. の問いに答えなさい。

Nearly everyone (1)is familiar with the concept of "news," but have you heard of "(2)personalized news?" Modern technology such as the Internet and smartphones means the number of media sources is now very large.

Thanks to this, people now have more options than ever from which to choose the news they
5 want to read. Though it offers people freedom of choice, there is a cost to such personalized news.

(3)The biggest problem with personalized news is that it does not expose people to a variety of ideas. Instead, personalized news feeds its readers, viewers and listeners what they want to read, see, and hear.

10 This *reinforces their current beliefs rather than offering them alternative ideas that go against their belief system. The effect this can have on a society is very worrying. A healthy society welcomes the free exchange of ideas. When people only receive news that tells them what they want to hear, (4)society can become divided.

For example, those who *identify with one political or social ideology sometimes view those
15 outside their group as the enemy. There is no simple solution to this problem.

However, one method of bringing people together is to raise awareness about the dangers of personalized news. If people have greater awareness about the ways in which personalized news *screens them from outside ideas, they will be more willing to seek out news that *contradicts their existing beliefs. (5)This can promote *mutual understanding and goodwill
20 among people with different ideas.

(246 words)

---

10 reinforce [rìːɪnfɔ́ːrs]：…を強固にする   14 identify with ...：…に共感する、傾倒する
18 screen A from B：AをBから遮断する   19 contradict [kà(ː)ntrədíkt]：…に反する
19 mutual [mjúːtʃu(ə)l]：相互の

CAN-DO List □ 🔍 〈知識・技能〉時や条件を表す副詞節について理解できる。
□ 💬 〈思考力・判断力・表現力〉パーソナライズされたニュースについて的確に理解できる。

1. この英文のタイトルとして最も適当なものを、次のa.～d.から選びなさい。　　　　（5点）

    a. 現代技術の進歩

    b.「ニュース」と「パーソナライズされたニュース」の違い

    c.「パーソナライズされたニュース」の危険性

    d. 世界で進む社会分裂

精 読問題 もう一度英文を読んで、次の問いに答えなさい。

2. 下線部(1)の意味として最も適当なものをa.～d.から一つ選びなさい。　　　　（4点）

    a. be acquainted with　　　　　　　　b. be new to

    c. be tired of　　　　　　　　　　　　d. get used to

3. 下線部(2)の意味として最も適当なものをa.～d.から一つ選びなさい。　　　　（4点）

    a. news which is based on personal experiences

    b. news which is not released by public organizations

    c. news which readers, viewers and listeners are interested in and want to know

    d. news which tells its readers, viewers and listeners wrong information

4. 下線部(3)の具体的な内容を、日本語で説明しなさい。　　　　（7点）

_____

5. 下線部(4)の内容がより具体的に述べられている一文を、本文中から抜き出しなさい。　　　　（6点）

_____

6. **文法** 下線部(5)の具体的な内容を、日本語で説明しなさい。　　　　（7点）

_____

7. **全体把握** 本文の内容と合っているものにはT、合っていないものにはFと答えなさい。（各2点）

    (ア) Everyone is familiar with the concept of personalized news.　　　　（　　　）

    (イ) What personalized news offers is what the receivers want.　　　　（　　　）

    (ウ) Personalized news offers people ideas that are different from their own beliefs.

    （　　　）

    (エ) Personalized news promotes mutual understanding among people with different ideas.

    （　　　）

Lesson **3** 時制②

Grammar 目標➡7分

1 次の各文を過去の場面に置きかえて、第2文を書きかえなさい。 (各3点)

1. We aren't hungry.　We have just had lunch.
→ We weren't hungry. _____

2. I don't know who she is.　I have never seen her before.
→ I didn't know who she was. _____

3. The house is dirty.　They haven't cleaned it for a week.
→ The house was dirty. _____

4. I am very tired.　I have been working hard all day.
→ I was very tired. _____

2 次の各文の( )内の動詞を現在完了形か過去完了形にしなさい。 (各3点)

1. Ruth is a good friend of mine.　I (know) her for a long time. _____

2. When we got home, we found that we (lose) the key.　We couldn't enter the house.

_____

3. She was badly injured but conscious and was able to tell what (happen).

_____

4. The man sitting next to me on the plane was very nervous.　He (not fly) before.

_____

Writing 目標➡3分

3 ( )内に与えられた語句を並べかえて、英文を完成しなさい。 (各5点)

1. もう何年もこの木には実がついていない。
(been / fruit / has / no / on / there / this tree) for many years.

_____

2. きのう何週間かぶりに雨が降った。
It rained yesterday (after / been / dry / had / it) for many weeks.

_____

3. 駅に着いたら、電車は2分前に出ていた。
When I arrived at the station, (found / had / I / left / the train) two minutes before.

_____

CAN-DO List □ 〈知識・技能〉現在[過去]完了形・現在[過去]完了進行形を適切に活用することができる。

Listening

目標➡5分　　テーマ 天候　英検®　 8～9

4 英文と質問を聞き、その答えとして最も適当なものを一つずつ選びなさい。　　（各5点）

1. ① Because the weather in the UK changes so often.
   ② Because the weather in the UK is perfectly predictable.
   ③ Because they can predict the weather easily.
   ④ Because they have such a culture and tradition.

2. ① An increase in damage from natural disasters.
   ② A drop in temperature in winter.
   ③ Global warming caused by human actions.
   ④ The emissions of greenhouse gases.

Rapid Reading

目標➡5分　　テーマ 気候変動　

5 （1）・（2）に入れるのに最も適当なものを一つずつ選びなさい。　　（各5点）

　Singapore is a big city where there are a lot of tall buildings.　However, we can also see a lot of trees and plants in cafés, parks, and shopping malls.　While we are living a city life, we （　1　） the forests in the parks in our city.

　My favorite memory of being very close to nature is when I was in kindergarten.　I liked to go out to a nearby forest with my mother.　This was my small, personal connection with nature.　Now, when are we aware of the climate crisis?　Probably, it is not until this sort of small piece of nature disappears from our cities that we will realize we are （　2　）.　On the small island where I live, natural surroundings are small.　However, no matter how small they are, they provide precious memories of experiencing nature for everybody living in this island. In order to stop the climate crisis, one important point is to be aware of what kind of nature is around us.

1. ① do not see any nature from
   ② have a chance to walk around
   ③ do not have something to do with
   ④ often carry out the plan of

2. ① going in the right direction for reducing climate change
   ② in the serious climate change crisis
   ③ in the middle of preventing climate change
   ④ trying to stop climate change

Reading 目標➡20分 　文法項目 現在[過去]完了形 　テーマ 気候変動 10

速 読問題 次の英文を2.5分で読んで、1. の問いに答えなさい。

(1)A third of the global population ——— 3.5 billion people ——— could be living in temperatures *inhospitable to human life in the next 50 years because of climate change, according to a recent study. The study, conducted by a team of five scientists and published by the National Academy of Sciences, found that most humans (2)have lived in places with an average

5　annual temperature between 51 and 59 degrees F（about 11℃ and 15℃）. By 2070, billions could be living in a climate currently found only in a select few places, like (3)Mecca in Saudi Arabia, where the average temperature is 86 F（30℃）.

　If current trends continue, more than 1 billion people in India, 500 million in Nigeria, and 100 million in the Niger and Sudan regions will be living with an average annual temperature of 84

10　F（29℃）, according to Tim Lenton, Professor of Climate Change and Earth Systems Science at the University of Exeter. That temperature is usually only seen in the Sahara Desert today, but it could cover 19 percent of the planet in 2070.

　The new study does not estimate how many people will leave their home countries in search of cooler climates. However, in 1990, *the Intergovernmental Panel on Climate Change had

15　stated that (4)this could be the greatest impact of climate change. Human migration is extremely difficult to *predict and responds to many factors other than heat alone, Lenton said. Still, he said his findings show that billions of people will be facing (5)conditions that could push them to leave their present homes.

(259 words)

---

²inhospitable[inhɑ(:)spítəb(ə)l]：（人間が住むのに）適さない
¹⁴the Intergovernmental Panel on Climate Change：気候変動に関する政府間パネル
¹⁶predict[prɪdíkt]：…を予測する

CAN-DO List 　□ 〈知識・技能〉現在[過去]完了形について理解できる。
　　　　　　　　　　□ 〈思考力・判断力・表現力〉気候変動の影響について的確に理解できる。

1. この英文のタイトルとして最も適当なものを、次のa.～d.から選びなさい。　　　　（5点）

   a. 生活に最適な気温

   b. 気候変動がもたらす影響

   c. 気候変動の原因

   d. 気候変動への対策

精 読問題 もう一度英文を読んで、次の問いに答えなさい。

2. 下線部(1)の人々に将来どんなことが起こると予測されていますか。最も適当なものをa.～d.から一つ選びなさい。　　　　（5点）

   a. 平均気温が11度から15度の土地で生活しなければならなくなる。

   b. 人間の生活に不適な気温の中で生活しなければならなくなる。

   c. サウジアラビアのメッカに移住しなければならなくなる。

   d. 人間が生活するのに適した気温を研究しなければならなくなる。

3. **文法** 下線部(2)の現在完了形と同じ用法を含む文をa.～d.から一つ選びなさい。　　　　（4点）

   a. Tomoki has just finished his homework.

   b. My hair is clean.　I have washed it.

   c. I have been to Australia several times.

   d. Mike has known Mary for more than 10 years.

4. 下線部(3)について、次の問いに英語で答えなさい。　　　　（5点）

What is the average temperature there?

_____

5. 下線部(4)の具体的な内容を説明した一文を完成させなさい。　　　　（完答6点）

人々が(　　　　　　　　　　　　)を求めて(　　　　　　　　　　　　)こと。

6. 下線部(5)の具体的な内容を、日本語で説明しなさい。　　　　（6点）

_____

_____

7. **全体把握** 本文の内容と合っているものにはT、合っていないものにはFと答えなさい。（各2点）

  (ア) In the next 50 years, 3.5 billion people could be living in the places where the temperatures are too low for humans to live.　　　　（　　　）

  (イ) Tim Lenton is a professor of Climate Change and Earth Systems Science at a university.　　　　（　　　）

  (ウ) An average annual temperature of 84 F is usually only seen in the Sahara Desert today.　　　　（　　　）

  (エ) The greatest impact of climate change could be human migration to find cooler places to live.　　　　（　　　）

  (オ) Tim Lenton does not insist that people will move to a cooler place because of climate change.　　　　（　　　）

Grammar 目標➡ 7分

1 次の各文の（　）内に下記の語（句）群から適当なものを選んで補いなさい。 （各2点）

1. You (　　　　　　　　) be Ann's sister.　You look just like her.
2. You (　　　　　　　　) be hungry.　You've just had lunch.
3. *A :* Where's Sue?　*B :* I'm not sure.　She (　　　　　　　　) be in the garden.
4. Liz has short hair now, but it (　　　　　　) be very long.
5. When he was young, he (　　　　　　) often walk in these woods.
   【can't / may / must / used to / would】

2 次の各文の（　）内に入れるのに最も適当なものを選んで補いなさい。 （各2点）

1. How can you say such a thing?　You (　　　　　　　　) be serious.
   【can't / might / must】
2. Your answers on these tests are too much alike.　You (　　　　　　　　).
   【can't have cheated / must cheat / must have cheated】
3. The plant is dead.　Maybe I (　　　　　　　) it more water.
   【must have given / should have given / should give】
4. We (　　　　　　　) our thick clothes.　The weather was really warm.
   【cannot have packed / might not have packed / needn't have packed】

Writing 目標➡ 5分

3 （　）内に与えられた語句を並べかえて、英文を完成しなさい。 （各4点）

1. 「私のバッグがどこにも見当たらない。」「レストランに置き忘れたのかもしれないよ。」
   "I can't find my bag anywhere."　"You (have / in / it / may / left) the restaurant."

2. きみは、彼のあやまちを笑うべきではなかったのです。
   You (at / have / his mistakes / laughed / shouldn't).

3. 我が社の新型機は、旧来型よりもずっと性能がよい。
   Our new type of machine is much better than (make / the type / to / we / used).

4. きみはぼくを起こさなくてもよかったのに。今日は仕事に行かなくてもいいのだ。
   You (have / me / needn't / up / woken).　I don't have to go to work today.

CAN-DO List □ 〈知識・技能〉いろいろな助動詞、過去に対する推量・後悔を適切に活用することができる。

4 それぞれのイラストについて4つの説明が読まれます。イラストに最も合っているものを一つず
つ選びなさい。 （各5点）

1.

① ② ③ ④

2.

① ② ③ ④

Rapid Reading 目標➡ 5分 　テーマ コミュニケーション

5 グラフを読み取って、問いに対する答えとして最も適当なものを一つずつ選びなさい。 （各5点）

About Stress that Workers Feel

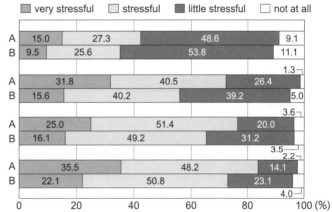

■ very stressful ☐ stressful ■ little stressful ☐ not at all

Stress caused by promotion and position
A: 15.0 | 27.3 | 48.6 | 9.1
B: 9.5 | 25.6 | 53.8 | 11.1

Stress caused by human relationships in a workplace
A: 31.8 | 40.5 | 26.4 | 1.3
B: 15.6 | 40.2 | 39.2 | 5.0

Stress caused by one's own role and sense of responsibility
A: 25.0 | 51.4 | 20.0 | 3.6
B: 16.1 | 49.2 | 31.2 | 3.5

Stress caused by one's job, such as the number of working hours
A: 35.5 | 48.2 | 14.1 | 2.2
B: 22.1 | 50.8 | 23.1 | 4.0

0　20　40　60　80　100 (%)

A：The person who hasn't received compliments

B：The person who has received compliments

1. Which is the item of stress that more than half of the subjects of this survey don't feel?
   ① Stress caused by promotion and position.
   ② Stress caused by human relationships.
   ③ Stress caused by their own roles and a sense of responsibility.
   ④ Stress caused by their jobs.

2. Which of the following statements is best supported by the above graph?
   ① Compliments impose stress on people.
   ② Compliments release people from stress.
   ③ People should play some sport to relieve stress.
   ④ People are so interested in their promotions.

速読問題 次の英文を2.5分で読んで、1. の問いに答えなさい。

"Everybody likes a compliment," Abraham Lincoln once wrote, and he was right. Do you remember the last time someone gave you a compliment? (1)It probably made you feel good, maybe even important. The right compliment can give both the giver and the receiver a *boost. Unfortunately, few people know how to give a good compliment. Here are a few

5 guidelines on how to make your compliments more effective.

First of all, only give genuine compliments. Most people can spot a fake compliment, and this insincere *flattery makes people feel worse, not better. For example, if your friend gives a really terrible presentation in class, (2)don't tell her, "That was a great speech." She'll know you are lying.

10 Second, (3)make your compliment specific. A general compliment such as "you look good today" has a lot less impact than a specific compliment such as "your new hairstyle is really cute." A specific compliment shows that you really notice the other person and is also more believable.

Finally, (4)explain your compliment. If you tell your friend "that hairstyle looks good on

15 you," you should next tell her why you think it looks good. For example, "your shorter hair makes your eyes easier to see" tells the other person why you are giving the compliment and proves the compliment is real.

(5)A good compliment will not only make the other person feel better, but you will feel better, too. To give a compliment, you have to really notice the good points of the other person.

20 And over time, it will become easier and easier to find the good points in other people. So why not start today? Find something good to say about another person, and then say it. You might be surprised at the reaction you get.

(294 words)

---

⁴boost[búːst]：高揚感、気分の盛り上がり　　⁷flattery[flǽt(ə)ri]：お世辞、ごますり

CAN-DO List 　□ 〈知識・技能〉いろいろな助動詞について理解できる。
　　　　　　　　□ 〈思考力・判断力・表現力〉ほめ言葉のかけ方について的確に理解できる。

1. この英文のタイトルとして最も適当なものを、次の a.～ d.から選びなさい。 （5点）

   a. A Genuine Compliment and a Fake Compliment

   b. A Specific Compliment and a General Compliment

   c. Compliment Needs Reasons

   d. How to Give a Good Compliment

精 読問題 もう一度英文を読んで、次の問いに答えなさい。

2. 下線部(1)を、It の具体的な内容を明らかにして、和訳しなさい。 （6点）

_____

3. 下線部(2)の理由を、日本語で説明しなさい。 （7点）

_____

4. 下線部(3)の理由を、日本語で説明しなさい。 （7点）

_____

5. 下線部(4)の具体的な内容を、日本語で説明しなさい。 （6点）

_____

6. 文法 下線部(5)とほぼ同じ内容を表す文を、本文中から抜き出しなさい。 （6点）

_____

7. 全体把握 次の問いに対する答えとして最も適当なものを、それぞれ下の a.～ d.のうちから一つ
ずつ選びなさい。 （各3点）

  (ア) Why do most people like to receive a compliment?

    a. Because it makes them feel better than other people.

    b. Because most people enjoy flattery.

    c. Because it makes other people feel good.

    d. Because it makes them feel important.

  (イ) Why should you not give an insincere compliment?

    a. Because most people can recognize an insincere compliment.

    b. Because an insincere compliment is hard to make specific.

    c. Because most insincere compliments make people feel too good.

    d. Because it's too hard to prove an insincere compliment.

  (ウ) How can you make your compliments believable?

    a. Make my compliments more general.

    b. Say the reason why I think the other person is good.

    c. Give specific compliments.

    d. Both b. and c.

Lesson 5 受動態

Grammar 目標➡7分

1 下線部を主語にした受動態の文を完成しなさい。(by ... は不要)　(各3点)

1. They have built a new hospital near the airport.

   A new hospital _____ .

2. I didn't know that they had changed the date of the meeting.

   I didn't know that the date of the meeting _____ .

3. They are typing the letters at the moment.

   The letters _____ .

4. They were cleaning the room when I arrived.

   The room _____ .

2 下線部を主語にした受動態の文を完成しなさい。　(各3点)

1. Yesterday a foreigner spoke to me in Japanese.

   Yesterday I _____ .

2. We must not throw away empty bottles.　(by ... は不要)

   Empty bottles _____ .

3. After her parents were killed in the war, her uncle brought up the child.

   After her parents were killed in the war, the child _____ .

4. The nurse took good care of the old woman.

   The old woman _____ .

Writing 目標➡3分

3 (　　)内に適語を補って、英文を完成しなさい。　(各2点)

1. チェロは演奏中、両脚にはさんで固定される。

   A cello is held between the legs while it is (　　　　　　) (　　　　　　).

2. そのコンピュータは、今使用中です。

   The computer (　　　　　　) (　　　　　　) (　　　　　　) at the moment.

3. 犬にかまれたことがありますか。

   Have you ever (　　　　　　) (　　　　　　) by a dog?

4. 彼女は、ハンドバッグを盗まれて泣いていた。

   She was weeping because her handbag (　　　　　　) been (　　　　　　).

5. 子供たちは手塩にかけて育てられています。

   The children are (　　　　　　) brought (　　　　　　) very carefully.

6. 私はこれまでそんな口のきき方をされたことはないよ。

   I have never been spoken (　　　　　　) (　　　　　　) that before.

CAN-DO List □ 🔍 〈知識・技能〉完了形・進行形の受動態、群動詞の受動態を適切に活用することができる。

4 それぞれの問いについて対話を聞き、答えとして最も適当なものを一つずつ選びなさい。(各5点)

1. 人々は何をしていますか。

2. スクランブル交差点が最も多い場所はどこですか。

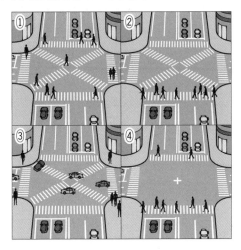

Rapid Reading　　目標➡5分　　　　　　　テーマ　インフラ

5 掲示を読み取って、問いに対する答えとして最も適当なものを一つずつ選びなさい。　(各5点)

Years of more roadwork ahead:

Montreal extends construction plans to a decade.

People in Montreal are struggling with traffic because there are more than 40 road construction sites in the city. There is construction work going on everywhere. The pace of the construction is another problem. It is so slow. A new highway is being constructed and, to complete it, a major highway will be closed down for the next month. Also, construction of a new train line is being carried out, and it will cause the closing down of an existing line for two years. People in Montreal are starting to complain about this situation.

---

1. Why are people in Montreal struggling with traffic?

① Because construction work in Montreal is stopped due to a lack of financial resources.

② Because lots of construction work is being carried out and the pace is slow.

③ Because most of the people in Montreal use their own cars.

④ Because there is enough road infrastructure in Montreal.

2. What problem will be caused by the construction of a new train line in Montreal?

① An existing highway will be closed down for two years.

② An existing train line will be closed down for two years.

③ Montreal will have to extend a train line in the next two months.

④ People in Montreal are complaining about the situation.

Reading　目標➡20分　文法項目　群動詞の受動態　テーマ　インフラ　◀))　16

速読問題　次の英文を3分で読んで、1. の問いに答えなさい。

(1)Nearly 80,000 tunnels, bridges and other vital components of Japan's road infrastructure are in a terrible state and badly in need of repair.　A survey by *the Ministry of Land, Infrastructure, Transport and Tourism (MLIT), which covered 770,000 bridges, tunnels, *pedestrian overpasses and other road infrastructure, identified 80,000 projects in need of
5　repair due to problems such as decay and cracks.　(2)Financial difficulties facing local governments mean that almost 80 percent of the repairs have yet to be carried out.

Percentage of infrastructure in need of repair　（%）				
	In good shape	Preventive maintenance phase	Early measures phase	Emergency measures phase
Bridge	41.4	48.9	（ ア ）	0.1
Tunnel	2.2	56.3	（ イ ）	（ ウ ）
Pedestrian overpass, others	31.9	52.8	15.2	0.1

(Source: MLIT)

In response to an accident in a tunnel in 2012, the central government ordered the nation's bridges, tunnels and other road infrastructure to be inspected every five years starting from 2014.　Most local governments managed to complete the first inspection by the end of fiscal
10　2018 and released (3)the results of these inspections, with each item of infrastructure classified in four phases.　According to the results, 68,369 bridges, or 9.5 percent of the roughly 720,000 total, need repairs within five years in what was labeled as the "early measures phase."　A further 682 bridges were *deemed to be in such a state as to require prompt action, which includes closing roads, in what was labeled the "emergency measures phase."

15　The survey found that 4,353 tunnels, or 40.9 percent of the roughly 10,000 total, need repairs within five years, while 63 tunnels were deemed to be in need of urgent work.　An additional 40,000 items of infrastructure, such as pedestrian overpasses, were in a (4)corresponding state. It said that 53,694 bridges, or 77.8 percent of the structures needing repairs, had not been fixed.

Roughly 90 percent of infrastructure that needs repair work is the responsibility of
20　prefectural governments or *local municipalities.　A lack of financial resources, coupled with opposition from residents over certain projects, have *hindered (5)demolition and repair work on aging infrastructure.　A professor of civil engineering urged local governments to create effective operational and maintenance plans "that include demolition and consolidation of infrastructure."

(322 words)

---

²the Ministry of Land, Infrastructure, Transport and Tourism (MLIT)：国土交通省
⁴pedestrian overpass：歩道橋　　¹³be deemed to ~：~と考えられる　　²⁰local municipality：地方自治体
²¹hinder[híndər]：…を妨げる、遅らせる

CAN-DO List　□ 🔍〈知識・技能〉群動詞の受動態について理解できる。
□ 💭〈思考力・判断力・表現力〉日本の道路インフラについて的確に理解できる。

1. この英文のタイトルとして最も適当なものを、次のa.〜d.から選びなさい。 （5点）

    a. A Lack of Financial Resources in Japan

    b. How Important Infrastructure Is

    c. Japan's Road Infrastructure in Need of Repair

    d. What Is Infrastructure?

精 読問題 もう一度英文を読んで、次の問いに答えなさい。

2. 下線部(1)の原因として具体的にどんなことが挙げられていますか。日本語で説明しなさい。（5点）

3. **文法** 下線部(2)について、財政難によってどのような状況が生じていますか。日本語で説明しなさい。 （6点）

4. 下線部(3)について、本文の内容と<u>合っていないもの</u>をa.〜d.から一つ選びなさい。 （5点）

    a. 道路インフラの状態は、4段階で評価された。

    b.「早期措置段階」と評価された橋は、調査対象となった橋全体の1割未満だった。

    c. 682本の橋は、すぐにも「早期措置段階」の状態になるだろうと判断された。

    d.「緊急措置段階」には、通行止めなどの迅速な対策が含まれている。

5. 下線部(4)の意味として最も適当なものをa.〜d.から一つ選びなさい。 （3点）

    a. different   b. difficult   c. important   d. similar

6. 道路インフラの点検結果を踏まえ、本文中の表(ア)〜(ウ)に入れる数値として最も適当なものを、下の選択肢から一つずつ選びなさい。 （各2点）

    (ア): _____   (イ): _____   (ウ): _____

    [0.6 / 0.8 / 9.5 / 40.9 / 77.8]

7. 下線部(5)が遅れている原因を、日本語で二つ列挙しなさい。 （各3点）

8. **全体把握** 本文の内容と合っているものにはT、合っていないものにはFと答えなさい。 （各2点）

    (ア) 国土交通省によると、橋やトンネルなどの道路インフラの補修がすでに8万件進行している。

                                                 （   ）

    (イ) 2012年に起こったあるトンネル事故を受けて、政府は橋やトンネルなどの道路インフラの点検を命じた。   （   ）

    (ウ) 地方自治体が管理する道路インフラの約9割が補修を必要としている。   （   ）

    (エ) 財源不足で地元住民の反対もあるが、高齢者に必要な道路インフラの補修作業は優先的に行われている。   （   ）

Lesson 6 to-不定詞

1 次の各文の（　　）内に入れるのに最も適当なものを選び、記号を補いなさい。　（各2点）

1. It is natural (　　　) parents to worry about their children.
   - a. for
   - b. from
   - c. of
   - d. with

2. It was careless (　　　) you to forget to invite Bob to the party.
   - a. for
   - b. in
   - c. of
   - d. to

3. It took (　　　) to finish his homework.
   - a. for him two hours
   - b. for two hours for him
   - c. him for two hours
   - d. him two hours

4. It (　　　) me thirty dollars to fix the door.
   - a. cost
   - b. demanded
   - c. needed
   - d. took

5. How (　　　) did it take you to walk to the station?
   - a. far
   - b. long
   - c. much
   - d. often

2 次の各文がほぼ同じ意味になるように、与えられた書き出しに続けて完成させなさい。（各4点）

1. It seemed that the old couple had no children.

   The old couple seemed to ＿＿＿＿＿＿＿＿＿＿＿＿＿＿＿＿＿＿＿＿＿＿＿＿.

2. It seems that he was late for the train.

   He seems to ＿＿＿＿＿＿＿＿＿＿＿＿＿＿＿＿＿＿＿＿＿＿＿＿＿＿＿.

3. It seemed that my brother had enjoyed his trip very much.

   My brother seemed to ＿＿＿＿＿＿＿＿＿＿＿＿＿＿＿＿＿＿＿＿＿＿.

3 （　　）内に与えられた語句を並べかえて、英文を完成しなさい。　（各5点）

1. 彼の足はとても大きくて、ふさわしい靴を見つけるのにひと苦労する。

   His feet are so big that it's (find / for / difficult / him / to) suitable shoes.

   ＿＿＿＿＿＿＿＿＿＿＿＿＿＿＿＿＿＿＿＿＿＿＿＿＿＿＿＿＿＿＿＿＿

2. 空港まで送ってくださり、ありがとうございました。

   It was (nice / of / take / to / you) me to the airport.　Thank you very much.

   ＿＿＿＿＿＿＿＿＿＿＿＿＿＿＿＿＿＿＿＿＿＿＿＿＿＿＿＿＿＿＿＿＿

3. 昔は通りで犬をたくさん見かけたが、最近はとても少なくなったようだ。

   I used to see a lot of dogs on our street, but (be / seem / there / to / very few) lately.

   ＿＿＿＿＿＿＿＿＿＿＿＿＿＿＿＿＿＿＿＿＿＿＿＿＿＿＿＿＿＿＿＿＿

CAN-DO List　□ 〈知識・技能〉不定詞の意味上の主語・It takes [costs] ... to ～、seem to-不定詞を適切に活用することができる。

4 英語の質問と、それに対する応答が 4 つ読まれます。応答として最も適当なものを一つずつ選びなさい。 (各 5 点)

1. ① ② ③ ④   2. ① ② ③ ④

Rapid Reading 目標➡ 5 分 テーマ 昆虫 英検®

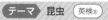

5 掲示を読み取って、問いに対する答えとして最も適当なものを一つずつ選びなさい。 (各 5 点)

Invitation
to participate in **the firefly watching**

The season has come around when we can see fireflies dancing in the dark.   This year many fireflies will be glowing along the riverbank, too.   Just as last year, Professor Asai will talk about the life of fireflies before watching.   Asai's lecture will be held outdoors.   In case of rain, it will be conducted in the gym.   The firefly watching will be carried out even if it rains.

*Advance reservations are not required.

*We will gather in the schoolyard this Saturday at 6:30 p.m.

*Friends and relatives are welcome, but children 12 and under should be accompanied by their parents.

*Don't forget to bring a flashlight.

Fireflies Study Society

---

1. How will Professor Asai's lecture and the firefly watching go if it rains this Saturday?

   ① They will be postponed until the next fine day.

   ② They will be canceled.

   ③ Only Asai's lecture will be carried out.

   ④ Both events will be carried out.

2. What do elementary school children have to do to take part in the firefly watching?

   ① Come with their classmates.

   ② Come with their parents.

   ③ Bring umbrellas.

   ④ Reserve in advance.

Reading 目標➡20分 文法項目 It takes [costs] … to ～ テーマ 生物 🔊 19

速読問題 次の英文を3分で読んで、1. の問いに答えなさい。

There are more than 37,000 species of spiders of different shapes and sizes in the world. The largest spiders live in the rain forests of South America and are known by the people who live there as "bird-eating spiders." These spiders can grow up to 28 centimeters long and, (1)as their name shows, they have been known to eat small birds.   On the other hand, the
5 smallest species of spider in the world lives in Western Samoa.   These spiders are less than half a millimeter long and live in plants that grow on mountain rocks.

(2)Some people like to keep spiders as pets.   *Tarantulas, for example, are very popular. They live in North America and can live for almost twenty-five years.   Most people, though, don't like to touch spiders, and a large number of people are afraid of them because they think
10 they are poisonous.   However, in fact, only thirty of the 37,000 species of spiders are very dangerous to humans.   (3)Spiders actually provide benefits to us by catching and eating insects such as flies and mosquitoes.

Spiders are very different from other animals because they make webs to catch the small insects they eat.   The *silk of a spider's web is produced by special *organs found in the lower
15 part of the body.   It is light, *elastic, and strong; it is five times stronger than steel.   The web will break up and finally return to nature as time passes, so (4)it would be perfect for making such things as fishing nets.   Some people have tried to keep spiders in order to make money.   (5)These businesses have never succeeded, however, because it takes 670,000 spiders to produce only half a kilogram of silk, and all of these spiders need living insects for their
20 food.   In addition, spiders are usually *solitary animals and need to be kept alone.

(307 words)

---

[7] tarantula[tərǽn(t)ʃ(ə)lə]：タランチュラ(毒グモ)   [14] silk[sílk]：(クモの)糸   [14] organ[ɔ́ːrg(ə)n]：器官
[15] elastic[ɪlǽstɪk]：伸縮性[弾力性]のある   [20] solitary[sá(ː)lətèri]：単独で生活する

CAN-DO List □ 🔍 〈知識・技能〉It takes [costs] … to ～について理解できる。
□ 💡 〈思考力・判断力・表現力〉クモの生態について的確に理解できる。

1. この英文で主に述べられているものを、次の a.～d. から選びなさい。 （5点）

   a．クモと人間の関わり   b．クモの種類と生態

   c．クモの巣の商業化の試み   d．ペットとしてのクモ

精 読問題 もう一度英文を読んで、次の問いに答えなさい。

2. 下線部(1)の as とほぼ同じ意味・用法の as を含む文を a.～d. から一つ選びなさい。 （3点）

   a．<u>As</u> I said yesterday, I'm thinking of changing my job.

   b．<u>As</u> the election approached, the violence got worse.

   c．Unfortunately, <u>as</u> I was parking the car, I hit the car behind it.

   d．We watched TV all evening <u>as</u> we had nothing better to do.

3. 下線部(2)について、他の人々はクモに対してどのような態度をとっていますか。日本語で説明しなさい。 （7点）

_____

_____

4. 下線部(3)の理由を、日本語で説明しなさい。 （7点）

_____

5. 下線部(4)の理由を、日本語で説明しなさい。 （7点）

_____

6. **文法** 下線部(5)の理由を、日本語で三つ箇条書きしなさい。 （各3点）

_____

_____

7. **全体把握** 本文の内容と合っているものには T、合っていないものには F と答えなさい。 （各1点）

   (ア) The largest spiders are called "bird-eating spiders" because birds eat them. (   )

   (イ) The smallest spiders live under mountain rocks in Western Samoa. (   )

   (ウ) Of the many species of spiders, less than 0.1 percent are very dangerous to humans.

                                                                        (   )

   (エ) The silk of a spider's web is produced by special organs found in the lower part of the body. (   )

   (オ) It is difficult to keep many spiders in one place. (   )

Lesson 7 動名詞

Grammar 目標➡ 7分

1 次の各文がほぼ同じ意味になるように、（　）内に適語を補いなさい。 (各2点)

1. Do you mind if I bring a friend to the party?
   Do you mind (　　　　　) (　　　　　) a friend to the party?

2. She complained that the room was too small.
   She complained about the room (　　　　　) too small.

3. The man was scolded because he didn't come to work on time.
   The man was scolded for (　　　　　) (　　　　　) to work on time.

4. He was not aware that he had done wrong.
   He was not aware of (　　　　　) (　　　　　) wrong.

5. She was ashamed that she had made the same mistake again.
   She was ashamed of (　　　　　) (　　　　　) the same mistake again.

2 次の各文の（　）内に下記の語群から適語を選び、動名詞にして補いなさい。 (各2点)

1. I am used to (　　　　　) on the left because I've lived in Japan for a long time.
2. I'm not looking forward to (　　　　　) to the dentist tomorrow.
3. What do you say to (　　　　　) lunch in the garden?
4. They objected to (　　　　　) on Sundays.
   【drive / go / have / work】

Writing 目標➡ 3分

3 （　）内に与えられた語句を並べかえて、英文を完成しなさい。 (各4点)

1. 私は、父が私たちにとても厳しかったことを覚えています。
   I remember (being / my father / us / very strict / with).

   _____

2. 約束の仕事をしなかったことで、あなた方は私たちの契約に違反しました。
   You have broken our agreement by (doing / not / promised / the work / you).

   _____

3. 彼女は待たされたことについて大きな声で不平を言った。
   She complained loudly (been / having / kept / of / waiting).

   _____

4. ここでは私がボスだ。何をするか指示されるなんてがまんならないぞ。
   I'm the boss here!　I'm (being / not / to / told / used) what to do.

   _____

CAN-DO List □ 〈知識・技能〉動名詞の意味上の主語・否定形・完了形、to の後に動名詞を続ける慣用表現を適切に活用することができる。

4 それぞれの問いについて対話を聞き、答えとして最も適当なものを一つずつ選びなさい。（各5点）

1. 大学で学生と教授が話をしています。

How many assignments does the man have in total?

① 3   ② 5   ③ 7   ④ 8

2. 夫婦が娘の誕生日会の計画を立てています。

What will the woman do for her daughter?

① She will bake a cake.   ② She will choose a birthday gift.

③ She will make chocolate.   ④ She will practice making a cake.

Rapid Reading 目標➡5分 テーマ スケジュール 英検®

5 Eメールを読み取って、問いに対する答えとして最も適当なものを一つずつ選びなさい。（各5点）

From: Edward Helen   To: undisclosed recipients
Date: October 14   Subject: About the next class

Dear Students,

  Please update your video conference software before our next class.　From the next class, we will have online classes.　If your software is not the latest version, you may not be able to join the next class.　Be careful, you cannot use your smartphone because the screen is too small to read presentation slides.

  Here is the schedule with the names of those who are going to make a presentation.

Date	Presenter	Presentation Title
October 21	Shoma Onishi	How to Improve English Pronunciation
October 28	Kazuma Kitamura	Let's Read Sherlock Holmes
November 4	Mayuko Nakano	My Favorite Things

Best regards,
Edward

From: Mayuko Nakano   To: Edward Helen
Date: October 16   Subject: About my presentation date

Dear Professor Helen,

  Thank you for your e-mail.　I have checked the presentation schedule.　However, would it be possible to ask you to change the schedule?　I cannot join the class on November 4th.　I have already asked Shoma whether he could switch his presentation date with mine, and he said OK.　So, I would like to make my presentation on October 21st. I'm really looking forward to joining your class.

Sincerely,
Mayuko

---

1. What do students have to do to join the online classes?

① Buy the latest model of smartphones.

② Download the video conference software to their smartphone.

③ Get their video conference software updated.

④ Send their presentation slides.

2. What is Mayuko asking Helen about?

① How to update the video conference software. ② The change of her presentation date.

③ The content of her presentation.   ④ The date of the next class.

Reading　目標➡20分　文法項目　to の後に動名詞を続ける慣用表現　テーマ　時間管理　🔊)) 22

速読問題 次の英文を3分で読んで、1.の問いに答えなさい。

(1)Time management is the ability to *allocate your time and resources in order to accomplish your objectives.　Skill in managing how you spend your time allows you to set and accomplish more goals in life, resulting in a sense of well-being because you are able to see the (2)fruits of your labors.　It gives you (3)a chance to achieve a balance between work and

5　personal life that can be more satisfying, (4)as opposed to restricting your activities to one area *at the expense of the other.　Effective managers also find that time management increases productivity.　The popular saying "Work smarter, not harder" applies here.　By focusing your energy on well-chosen activities, you can actually see your results.　This in itself can be motivating, which can then increase your *drive to achieve even more.

10　Managing your time also reduces stress levels.　Taking control of your time means taking control of your life.　This results in a feeling that you are in charge.　"I exercised today, and now I can go back and study for the exam with a clear head" is an example of (5)this, which is better than thinking "I have no time, I have no life.　I didn't exercise, and now I don't even have the energy to study for this exam."　Time management gives you more time to enjoy the

15　activities that are important to you, such as spending time with family and friends, reading, exercising, and pursuing your favorite hobbies.　This means you are better able to enjoy a varied, balanced life.　As human beings, we have many dimensions.　We are not meant to simply work.　Most of us have the need to be many things——a friend, a partner, a family member, part of a community.　As you *incorporate many different elements into your life,

20　each of those elements becomes more satisfying with your involvement in the others.

(312 words)

---

¹allocate[ǽləkèɪt]：…を分配する　⁶at the expense of ...：…を犠牲にして
⁹drive[dráɪv]：意欲、やる気　¹⁹incorporate[ɪnkɔ́ːrpərèɪt]：…を組み入れる

CAN-DO List　☐ 〈知識・技能〉to の後に動名詞を続ける慣用表現について理解できる。
☐ 〈思考力・判断力・表現力〉時間管理のメリットについて的確に理解できる。

	Grammar	Writing	Listening	Rapid Reading	Reading	Total
	/18	/16	/10	/10	/46	/100

1. この英文のタイトルとして最も適当なものを、次のa.～d.から選びなさい。 （5点）

   a．A Lot of Different Elements in Your Life

   b．Becoming an Effective Manager at Work

   c．Roles of Time Management in Your Life

   d．Time Management Keeps You Busier

精 読問題 もう一度英文を読んで、次の問いに答えなさい。

2. 下線部(1)を行う目的を、15字以内の日本語で説明しなさい。 （5点）

   □□□□□□□□□□□□□□□□□□□□□□□□

3. 下線部(2)とほぼ同じ意味を表す単語を、第1パラグラフから抜き出しなさい。また、その日本語の意味も答えなさい。 （各4点）

   単語：＿＿＿＿＿＿＿＿＿＿＿＿＿   意味：＿＿＿＿＿＿＿＿＿＿＿＿＿

4. 下線部(3)の具体的な内容を、日本語で説明しなさい。 （7点）

5. **文法** 下線部(4)の意味として最も適当なものをa.～d.から一つ選びなさい。 （4点）

   a．because of   b．for the purpose of

   c．in addition to   d．in contrast with

6. 下線部(5)の具体的な内容を、日本語で説明しなさい。 （7点）

7. **全体把握** 次の各文の□□□に入れるのに最も適当なものを、それぞれ下のa.～d.のうちから一つずつ選びなさい。 （各5点）

  (ア) Effective managers find that productivity □□□．

     a．goes up with good time management

     b．improves the ability to manage time

     c．is increased by working harder

     d．restricts activities to one area

  (イ) As a successful example of time management, it gives us □□□．

     a．more energy to work harder

     b．more time to stay with family and friends

     c．the drive to reduce stress levels

     d．the motivation to find a new hobby

Grammar　目標➡ 7分

1 次の各文の(　　)内から適当なほうを選びなさい。　　　　　　　　　　(各3点)

1. They found the lifeboat (floating / floated) upside down.
2. Do they always keep the dog (tying / tied) to the gate?
3. Can you easily make yourself (understanding / understood) in English?
4. We had the carpenter (build / built) a large cabinet.
5. We're going to have a new cupboard (build / built) in the kitchen.
6. My wife had her passport (steal / stolen).

2 次の各文の(　　)内の動詞を現在分詞か過去分詞にしなさい。　　　　　(各2点)

1. (Realize) that he had a talent for music, he decided to become a professional singer.
　　　　　　　　　　　　　　　　　　　　　　　　　　　　　＿＿＿＿＿＿＿＿
2. (Write) in plain English, this novel is easy to read.　　　　＿＿＿＿＿＿＿＿
3. (Feel) very hungry, Mike ordered a double hamburger.　　＿＿＿＿＿＿＿＿
4. (View) from this angle, the building looks bigger than it really is.　＿＿＿＿＿＿＿＿
5. Can you walk in a straight line with your eyes (close)?　　＿＿＿＿＿＿＿＿

Writing　目標➡ 3分

3 (　　)内に与えられた語句を並べかえて、英文を完成しなさい。　　　(各4点)

1. ネコが近づいて来るのを見て、スズメは飛び去った。

The sparrow flew away (approaching / it / saw / the cat / when).

＿＿＿＿＿＿＿＿＿＿＿＿＿＿＿＿＿＿＿＿＿＿＿＿＿＿＿＿＿＿＿＿＿＿＿

2. 言葉が話されているのを耳で聞いて学ぶのは、よい学習法である。

Studying (it / by / hearing / a language / spoken) is a good way of learning.

＿＿＿＿＿＿＿＿＿＿＿＿＿＿＿＿＿＿＿＿＿＿＿＿＿＿＿＿＿＿＿＿＿＿＿

3. 新聞は家に配達してもらっているのですか。それとも、出勤途中で買うのですか。

Do you (a newspaper / delivered / have / to / your home), or do you buy one on your way to work?

＿＿＿＿＿＿＿＿＿＿＿＿＿＿＿＿＿＿＿＿＿＿＿＿＿＿＿＿＿＿＿＿＿＿＿

4. 私は倒れて、ドアに頭をぶつけて切ってしまった。

I fell, (against / and / my head / striking / the door) cutting it.

＿＿＿＿＿＿＿＿＿＿＿＿＿＿＿＿＿＿＿＿＿＿＿＿＿＿＿＿＿＿＿＿＿＿＿

CAN-DO List　□　〈知識・技能〉S＋V＋O＋C(分詞)、現在[過去]分詞ではじまる分詞構文・with の後ろに続く名詞と分詞を適切に活用することができる。

4 長めの対話を一つ聞き、問いの答えとして最も適当なものを一つずつ選びなさい。対話の前に
Situation が読み上げられます。　　　　　　　　　　　　　　　　　　　　　　（各5点）

Situation：A female tourist is asking a male tourist about what he did on that day.

1. How did the man feel about the attitude of the clerk?
   ① He thought it was nice.
   ② He felt angry about it.
   ③ He couldn't understand what the clerk said.
   ④ He thought it looked strange.

2. When did the man drink the espresso coffee?
   ① In the morning.　　　　　　　② In the middle of shopping.
   ③ After shopping.　　　　　　　④ The next day.

Rapid Reading 目標➡5分 テーマ 標識 GTEC®

5 英文を読んで、問いに対する答えとして最も適当なものを一つずつ選びなさい。　（各5点）

　　Most of the signs at the railway stations are written in four languages: Japanese, English, Chinese and Korean.　Sometimes pictograms are added to these four languages.　So, even if you don't understand any of these four languages, you may understand the meaning of the pictograms.　If foreigners who cannot understand any of these languages are looking for elevators, restrooms, or exits, these pictures are helpful.　Pictograms are a real universal language.

1. What is this passage mainly about?
   ① How to get on the train in a foreign country.
   ② Pictograms as a universal language.
   ③ Problems when you travel abroad.
   ④ The importance of learning English.

2. Which of the following statements is true about a pictogram?
   ① It is a large printed picture or notice in a public place, often used to advertise something.
   ② It is a sign, action or sound that sends a particular message.
   ③ It is a sign like an arrow used to show direction or the position of something.
   ④ It is a visual sign that represents something like information or attention.

Reading 　目標➡20分　　文法項目 S+V+O+C(分詞)　テーマ 旅行　　🔊 24

速 読問題 次の英文を3分で読んで、1. の問いに答えなさい。

During her summer vacation, a young Austrian student named Margo Fenster went on a walking tour in the north of Scotland.　She visited *Fort William and *Inverness and enjoyed the lake and mountain scenery.　Most of the time (1)she tried to keep to the side roads because she wanted to see how the local people lived.　She also wanted to get away from cars and

5　trucks as much as possible.　(2)She hiked past farmhouses and fields full of sheep.　It was near the end of the summer, and here and there she could see farmers on tractors harvesting their crops.　The weather was fine and unusually warm.

Suddenly dark clouds appeared in the sky and within a quarter of an hour a thunderstorm started.　There was heavy rain and thunder and lightning.　Miss Fenster came to a small

10　village, and she found a pub.　(3)This was excellent because it was just lunchtime.

Miss Fenster went into the pub.　Inside, to the right of the bar, there was a small, simple dining room.　She sat down by the window and tried to order lunch.　(4)Her English was poor, however, and she could not make herself understood.

There was no menu that she could point to, and she was very hungry after walking all

15　morning.　Suddenly she had an idea.　In the small hotels where she always stayed, the usual breakfast was bacon and eggs and mushrooms.　She took out a piece of paper and a pencil and (5)drew a simple picture of a mushroom.　The waiter looked at the drawing, said "Right.　I understand," and went out of the room.

Miss Fenster was pleased and sat waiting hungrily for her lunch.　But a few minutes later,

20　when the waiter appeared again, he was not bringing a plate of hot food.　He was holding an umbrella.

(304 words)

---

²Fort William：フォートウィリアム（スコットランド北部の町）
²Inverness［invərnés］：インバネス（Fort William よりさらに北方の古都）

34 ｜ CAN-DO List ☐ 🔘 〈知識・技能〉S+V+O+C(分詞)について理解できる。
☐ 📖 〈思考力・判断力・表現力〉ある学生の旅行に関するストーリーの展開を的確に理解できる。

1. この英文のタイトルとして最も適当なものを、次の a.～ d.から選びなさい。 （5点）

   a. A Change of the Weather   b. A Picture of a Mushroom

   c. Traditional Dishes in Scotland   d. How People in Scotland Live

精 **読問題** もう一度英文を読んで、次の問いに答えなさい。

2. 下線部(1)の理由を、日本語で二つ説明しなさい。 （各3点）

_____

3. **文法** 下線部(2)について、次の問いに英語で答えなさい。 （4点）

While Miss Fenster hiked past farmhouses and fields full of sheep, what were farmers doing?

_____

4. 下線部(3)の具体的な内容を、日本語で説明しなさい。 （5点）

_____

5. **文法** 下線部(4)を和訳しなさい。 （5点）

_____

6. 下線部(5)でフェンスターはウエイターに何を伝えようとしたのですか。日本語で簡単に説明しなさい。 （5点）

_____

7. **全体把握** 本文の内容と合っているものを、それぞれ下の a.～ e.のうちから一つずつ選びなさい。

（各2点）

(ア) a. Miss Fenster was looking for a job.

    b. Miss Fenster was riding a new bicycle.

    c. Miss Fenster was hunting sheep.

    d. Miss Fenster was driving a truck.

    e. Miss Fenster was interested in the people of Scotland.

(イ) a. Miss Fenster stayed in the best hotel in Inverness.

    b. Miss Fenster was good at drawing.

    c. The waiter did not understand what Miss Fenster wanted.

    d. In Scotland people eat lunch under an umbrella.

    e. There was a menu, but Miss Fenster couldn't read it.

(ウ) a. English is spoken in Austria.

    b. There were not many cars or trucks on the main roads in Scotland.

    c. Miss Fenster wanted to have lunch at the pub she had found.

    d. People in Scotland eat bacon and eggs and mushrooms for lunch.

    e. People in Scotland don't carry an umbrella even when it is raining.

Grammar 目標➡7分

1 次の各文の（　）内に入れるのに最も適当なものを選んで補いなさい。　　　（各2点）

1. Your English is improving.　It's getting (　　　　　　　　) better.
   【better and / better to / good and】

2. The older we grow, (　　　　　　　　) our memory becomes.
   【the weak / the weaker / too weak】

3. She looks (　　　　　　　) prettier with long hair than with short hair.
   【more / much / much more】

4. Ann (　　　　　　　　) longer works here.　She left last month.
   【any / much / no】

2 次の各文がほぼ同じ意味になるように、（　）内に適語を補いなさい。　　　（各3点）

1. The elephant is the largest land animal.
   The elephant is (　　　　　　) (　　　　　　　) any other land animal.

2. The church is the oldest building in the town.
   The church is older than (　　　　　　) other (　　　　　　) in the town.

3. Time is the most precious thing of all.
   (　　　　　　　) is more precious than time.

4. I have never eaten such a good hamburger as this.
   This is the (　　　　　　) hamburger I have (　　　　　　) eaten.

Writing 目標➡5分

3 （　）内に適語を補って、英文を完成しなさい。　　　（各3点）

1. 庭は、小さければ小さいほど手入れが容易である。
   The smaller a garden is, the (　　　　　　　) it is to look (　　　　　).

2. その計画について考えれば考えるほど、私は嫌になってきた。
   The (　　　　　　) I thought about the plan, the (　　　　　　) I liked it.

3. アンは、ジルよりもテニスがはるかに上手だ。
   Ann is (　　　　　　) better (　　　　　　) tennis than Jill.

4. 彼女は以前はフランス語を勉強していたが、今はもうしていない。
   She used to study French, but she doesn't study it (　　　　　) (　　　　　).

5. 朝早く散歩することほど楽しいことはありません。
   (　　　　　　) is (　　　　　　) pleasant than to take a walk early in the morning.

6. その馬が農場でいちばん美しい生き物だった。
   (　　　　　　) other (　　　　　　) in the farm was more beautiful than the horse.

7. これは、私が今までにしなければならなかった決心の中でも最もむずかしい決心です。
   This is the most difficult decision I've (　　　　　) (　　　　　) to make.

　CAN-DO List　□ 🔎　〈知識・技能〉比較級を用いた慣用表現、最上級の意味を表す比較表現を適切に活用することができる。

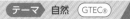

4 それぞれのイラストについて4つの説明が読まれます。イラストに最も合っているものを一つずつ選びなさい。 （各5点）

1.

① ② ③ ④

2.

the summit of Mt.Asahi

① ② ③ ④

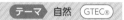

5 パンフレットを読み取って、問いに対する答えとして最も適当なものを一つずつ選びなさい。 （各5点）

Nature Tours 〔Campaign Now Under Way〕
"Yellowstone National Park, the kingdom of color"

Visit Yellowstone and experience the world's first national park. Nature Tours has the following two fun tours in Yellowstone.

Tour 1
Marvel at a volcano's hidden power rising up in colorful hot springs and geysers (a natural spring that sometimes sends hot water or steam up into the air).
Weekdays: 9:00 a.m.―12:00 at noon **Weekends:** 10:00 a.m.―2:00 p.m.
Price for each person: $200 / $230 (including "special lunch" as an option, only on weekends)
We will visit two hot springs, **Morning Glory Pool** and **Grand Prismatic Spring**, but we can't bathe.

Tour 2
Explore mountains, forests and lakes to watch bison and grizzly bears and witness the drama of the natural world.
Everyday in summer (May―September): 1:00 p.m.―4:30 p.m.
Price for each person: $100
We will walk 7 kilometers in all, so casual shoes with flexible rubber soles are a must.

Contact us Nature Tours: www.naturetours.com

---

1. What are the conditions to enjoy Morning Glory Pool and Grand Prismatic Spring, and to watch wildlife in one day?
   ① Participating in Tour 1 on weekdays. ② Participating in Tour 2 in July.
   ③ Participating in both Tour 1 and Tour 2 on weekdays in August.
   ④ Participating in both Tour 1 and Tour 2 in March.

2. Which of the following statements is true?
   ① We can enjoy taking a bath in Tour 1.
   ② We can watch animals of the forest in winter by joining Tour 2.
   ③ It is possible for us to participate in both tours in March.
   ④ We can have lunch at an additional cost of $30 in Tour 1 on weekends.

Reading　目標➡20分　文法項目　比較級を用いた慣用表現　テーマ　自然　🔊 27

速読問題 次の英文を2.5分で読んで、1. の問いに答えなさい。

The year 1988 will not be forgotten for a long time at Yellowstone National Park. (1)Fires broke out in June and (2)burned fiercely until September. (3)The flames were not put out completely until November. They covered almost half of the vast park. What caused such huge fires? There are several answers to this question.

5　*Lodgepole pines make up 80 percent of the park's forests. These trees grow quickly, but they only live about 200 years. Then many of the pines die and are blown down by high winds. The trees lie on the forest floor for many years. In wet forests they will decay and turn back into soil, but it is too dry for (4)this to happen in Yellowstone. (5)In 1988, dead wood, which burns easily, covered the forest floor.

10　Yellowstone usually gets a lot of snow in winter. When the snow melts, it provides water for the plants. However, for six winters in the 1980s, little snow had fallen. Rain also usually falls during the summer months, but 1988 was the driest summer in 116 years.

Several fires started in and near the park in June. Some of them were caused by human carelessness. Others were started by violent forces of nature such as lightning. Since little

15　rain fell in June, the fires became larger and larger. More than 17,000 acres had burned by July 21.

On June 23, strong winds blew the fires into other areas of the park. Firefighters battled the *blazes, but they had little success. On August 20, winds measuring 80 miles per hour swept through the park. (6)This day became known as Black Saturday. Fires that had

20　almost died out came back to life. The firefighters tried very hard, but they couldn't control the fires. The worst of the fires were put out when snow and rain began to fall in September. The remaining fires were put out by heavy snows in November.　　　(322 words)

---

⁵lodgepole pine：ロッジポールパイン（マツの木の一種）　　¹⁸blaze[bléɪz]：炎、火災

CAN-DO List　☐ 🔍 〈知識・技能〉比較級を用いた慣用表現について理解できる。
☐ 💬 〈思考力・判断力・表現力〉イエローストーン国立公園の山火事について的確に理解できる。

1. この英文のタイトルとして最も適当なものを、次の a.～ d.から選びなさい。 （5点）

   a. A Battle Against Forest Fires

   b. Extensive Damage to Yellowstone National Park

   c. Violent Forces of Nature

   d. What Caused the 1988 Fires at Yellowstone National Park?

精 読問題 もう一度英文を読んで、次の問いに答えなさい。

2. 下線部(1)の内容がより具体的に述べられているパラグラフの最初の一文を抜き出しなさい。（5点）

3. 下線部(2)の内容がより具体的に述べられている一文を、本文中から抜き出しなさい。 （5点）

4. 下線部(3)の内容がより具体的に述べられている一文を、本文中から抜き出しなさい。 （5点）

5. 下線部(4)の this の指す具体的な内容を、日本語で説明しなさい。 （3点）

6. 文法 下線部(5)の原因がより具体的に述べられているパラグラフの最初の一文を抜き出しなさい。

（5点）

7. 下線部(6)の理由を、日本語で説明しなさい。 （7点）

8. 全体把握 次の各文を起きた順序に並べかえなさい。 （各1点）

   (ア) Several fires started in and near Yellowstone National Park.

   (イ) Because of winds measuring 80 miles per hour, fires that had almost died out came back to life.

   (ウ) More than 17,000 acres had burned.

   (エ) Snow and rain put out the worst of the fires.

   (オ) Strong winds blew the fires into other areas of the park.

   (カ) The fires were put out completely by heavy snows.

   （ ア ） → （   ） → （   ） → （   ） → （   ） → （ カ ）

Lesson 10 関係詞①

Grammar　目標➡7分

1 次の各文の（　）内に下記の語群から適語を選んで補いなさい。　(各2点)

1. My grandfather was born in the year (　　　　　) the war ended.
2. The reason (　　　　　) we are late is that our car broke down.
3. There is always a queen bee in the place (　　　　　) bees live.
4. This is (　　　　　) we came to know each other.
5. Paula was ill yesterday.　That's (　　　　　) she didn't come to class.
6. The time will come (　　　　　) every one of us uses a computer.
　【how / when / where / why】

2 次の各文の（　）内に入れるのに最も適当なものを選び、記号を補いなさい。　(各2点)

1. This is the book (　　　) the other day.
　a. I told you about　　　　　　　b. that I spoke
　c. which I told you　　　　　　　d. which I told you to
2. The magician performed a trick (　　　) he made a rabbit disappear.
　a. how　　　　b. in that　　　　c. in which　　　d. which
3. The period (　　　) human beings learned to make tools of iron is called the Iron Age.
　a. in that　　　b. in which　　　c. of which　　　d. which
4. Adults often envy the ease (　　　) children learn another language.
　a. for what　　　b. of which　　　c. with that　　　d. with which
5. In only a short time, computers have profoundly changed the way in (　　　) many kinds of work are done.
　a. that　　　　b. which　　　　c. what　　　　d. how

Writing　目標➡3分

3 （　）内に与えられた語句を並べかえて、英文を完成しなさい。　(各5点)

1. 私たちが車を修理してもらった修理工場の名前が思い出せません。
　I can't remember the name of the garage (had / repaired / the car / we / where).

2. 電話で話をした女性に、あなたは外出していると言われました。
　(I / on / spoke / the phone / the woman / to) told me you were out.

3. 宇宙のどこかに、私たちと同じような生命体のいる惑星が存在しているかもしれない。
　Somewhere in the universe, (a planet / be / may / on / there / which) there is some form of life like ours.

CAN-DO List ☐ 〇 〈知識・技能〉関係副詞、前置詞と関係代名詞を適切に活用することができる。

4 長めの英文を一つ聞き、問いの答えとして最も適当なものを一つずつ選びなさい。 （各5点）

1. Who is the speaker looking for?
   ① The person who offers network service.
   ② The person who can communicate well.
   ③ The person who can write French or Spanish.
   ④ The person who finished university.

2. What is the listener good at doing?
   ① Teaching communication skills.
   ② Setting up computers.
   ③ Designing web pages.
   ④ Making instruction manuals.

Rapid Reading 目標➡ 5分 〈テーマ〉職業

5 掲示を読み取って、問いに対する答えとして最も適当なものを一つずつ選びなさい。 （各5点）

Experienced Web Designer NEEDED

Web Designer

ABC University in Seattle is looking for a creative web designer. We are currently underway for founding Tokyo Branch of ABC University.

Working at Tokyo Branch. Must be a Japanese. A lot of experience is needed. A good command of English would be good but is not essential. This is a full-time position with wages paid monthly. Benefits include full medical insurance and paid vacations.

E-mail for details: info@abc.edu

---

1. Who should respond to the notice?
   ① People who are looking for a part-time job.
   ② People who can use previous experience.
   ③ People who can relocate to Seattle.
   ④ Only people with a good command of English.

2. What benefits are included?
   ① Hourly breaks.
   ② Taking days off.
   ③ Learning English in Seattle.
   ④ Opportunities to travel to Seattle.

Reading

目標➡20分　文法項目 前置詞と関係代名詞　テーマ 職業　🔊 29

速読問題 次の英文を3分で読んで、1.の問いに答えなさい。

　　Hunting for a job is a painful experience, but one that nearly everyone must endure at least once in a lifetime.　Books are published and magazine articles are written on the subject. They all try to tell job-seekers what they should do or avoid doing in order (1)to survive and to win the game.　They can't calm the nervous applicant (and what applicant is not nervous?), but they do offer some advice that deserves consideration.

　　To begin with, it is not a good idea to be late.　Job interviewers don't think very highly of the candidate who arrives twenty minutes after the appointed time, offering no apology or (2)explaining that he couldn't find the street, and that his watch is slow.　The wise job-seeker explores the place the day before to make sure that he can locate the building, the right floor, and the office in which the interview will take place; at the same time he looks around to see what the employees are wearing and how they seem to behave at work.　(3)The next day he arrives early for the appointment.　It does not matter if the employer's secretary recognizes him and mentions his first visit to her boss.　The eager candidate can be regarded as smart, thoughtful, and *well-organized——three points in his favor before he has said a word.

　　Most *personnel managers admit that they know within the first few minutes of the meeting whether or not they want to hire (4)the person to whom they are talking.　This is particularly true when their first reaction to the applicant is negative, when the man or woman has made a disastrous first impression.　But what makes a *good* impression?　(5)What counts?　Being on time does, as we have seen; then, appearance.　It is essential for the candidate to be dressed properly, and to look alert, pleasant, and interested.　It is also very important to look the interviewer in the eyes because this "eye contact" gives a strong impression of sincerity and *openness.

(335 words)

---

¹⁴well-organized[wèl ɔ́ːrɡənàɪzd]：十分に労働意欲がある　　¹⁵personnel[pə̀ːrsənél]：人事担当の
²²openness[óʊp(ə)nnəs]：率直さ

CAN-DO List　☐ 🔍〈知識・技能〉前置詞と関係代名詞について理解できる。
　　　　　　　　☐ 💭〈思考力・判断力・表現力〉就職活動のアドバイスについて的確に理解できる。

1. この英文で、面接試験に成功するために最も大切なものとして述べられているものを、次の a.～ d. から選びなさい。 （5点）

  a. あらかじめ、面接試験について研究しておくこと。

  b. 前日に面接会場を訪れておくこと。

  c. 好ましい第一印象を与えること。

  d. 面接担当者に自分を十分にアピールすること。

精 読問題 もう一度英文を読んで、次の問いに答えなさい。

2. 下線部⑴の具体的な内容として最も適当なものを a.～ d. から一つ選びなさい。 （3点）

  a. to calm the nervous applicant   b. to get a job

  c. to hunt for a job   d. to offer some good advice

3. 文法 下線部⑵の状況を避けるためにはどうすればよいか、日本語で説明しなさい。 （7点）

_____

4. 下線部⑶の生み出す効果を、日本語で説明しなさい。 （7点）

_____

5. 文法 下線部⑷とほぼ同じ内容を表す2語から成る表現を、本文中から抜き出しなさい。 （7点）

_____

6. 下線部⑸を次のように書きかえたとき、（   ）内に本文中の1語を書き入れなさい。 （5点）

To make a good impression, what is (   )?

7. 全体把握 次の各文の [____] に入れるのに最も適当なものを、それぞれ下の a.～ d. のうちから一つずつ選びなさい。 （各3点）

  (ア) Books on hunting for a job [____].

   a. are painful to read   b. list likely employers

   c. make people nervous   d. give useful guidance

  (イ) Job applicants should [____].

   a. avoid being recognized if they arrive in advance

   b. visit the office a day early to avoid getting lost

   c. arrive after the appointed time to be regarded as smart

   d. mention their thoughts about employees' clothing and behavior

  (ウ) It's important to make a good first impression because [____].

   a. personnel managers make their hiring decisions very quickly

   b. candidates are dressed well and are interested

   c. interviewers are impressed by sincere "eye-contact"

   d. applicants otherwise react negatively

Lesson 11 関係詞②

Grammar 目標➡7分

1 下記の語句群から適当なものを選んで、英文を完成しなさい。 (各2点)

1. All right, doctor, I'll do _____.
2. The teacher tested the students to see if they remembered _____.
3. The full story of _____ will never be known.
4. Many people have to be careful of _____. They get fat easily.
5. He believes in saying _____, even when it upsets people.

【what he thinks / what really happened / what they eat / what they had learned / what you say】

2 次の各文の( )内に適当な関係代名詞を補いなさい。 (各2点)

1. エイミーは、車が故障して、ひどく機嫌が悪かった。

   Amy, ( ) car had broken down, was in a very bad mood.
2. 彼はお皿を全部割ってしまい、母親をひどく怒らせた。

   He broke all the dishes, ( ) made his mother very angry.
3. チョコレートは、彼女の大好物ですが、彼女を太らせます。

   Chocolate, ( ) she is very fond of, makes her fat.
4. チョウの種類は多く、そのほとんどが色彩豊かである。

   There are many types of butterflies, most of ( ) are very colorful.

Writing 目標➡3分

3 ( )内に与えられた語句を並べかえて、英文を完成しなさい。 (各4点)

1. 自分のものではないものを取る権利は、きみにはない。

   You don't (have / take / the right / to / what) is not yours.

   _____

2. 木々の間を通して、小さな農場らしきものが見えた。

   Through the trees they could see (a small / farm / be / seemed / to / what).

   _____

3. ロンドンはかつて世界最大の都市でしたが、今人口は減少しています。

   The population of London, (in / the largest city / the world / was once / which), is now decreasing.

   _____

4. カーター氏は、昨夜電話で話をしたのですが、私たちの計画にとても興味をもっています。

   Mr. Carter, (I / on / spoke / the phone / to whom) last night, is very interested in our plan.

   _____

CAN-DO List □ 〈知識・技能〉関係代名詞の what、関係代名詞の非制限用法を適切に活用することができる。

4 長めの対話を一つ聞き、問いの答えとして最も適当なものを一つずつ選びなさい。 （各5点）

1. What did the man take from a Japanese comic book?
   ① Only a character.
   ② Only a car.
   ③ Both a character and a car.
   ④ Either a character or a car.

2. What does the woman want to know about the cartoon car?
   ① What the name of the car is.
   ② The country in which the car is made.
   ③ Whether the man created the car or not.
   ④ When the man learned about the car.

Rapid Reading 目標➡5分 テーマ 漫画 英検®

5 （1）・（2）に入れるのに最も適当なものを一つずつ選びなさい。 （各5点）

Charles Schulz was born in Minnesota in 1922. From when he was very young, comics played an important part in his life, and throughout his youth he and his father read newspaper cartoons together. Schulz always knew that he wanted to be a cartoonist in the future. He had to *put his artistic ambitions on hold during World War II, but after being *discharged in 1945, he returned to his hometown to (1). His world-famous comic, Peanuts, first appeared in national newspapers in 1950, and eventually (2). When Schulz announced his retirement in 1999, Peanuts was published in more than 2,600 newspapers worldwide. He passed away on February 12, 2000, just hours before the final Peanuts Sunday *strip was published in newspapers.

> ⁴put ... on hold：…を保留[延期]する   ⁴discharge[dɪstʃɑ́ːrdʒ]：…を除隊させる
> ⁸strip[stríp]：数コマの漫画

1. ① become a movie star
   ② give up his dream
   ③ pursue a cartooning career
   ④ read comic books
2. ① became an international success
   ② didn't gain popularity
   ③ he lost his job
   ④ he became disappointed

速 読問題 次の英文を３分で読んで、１．の問いに答えなさい。

(1)For Sparky, school was quite hopeless.　He failed every subject in the eighth grade.　He failed physics in high school, getting a grade of zero.　Sparky also failed *Latin, mathematics and English.　He didn't do much better in sports.　Although he managed to become a member of the school's golf team, he lost the only important match of the season.　There was

5　a *consolation match, but he lost that, too.

　All through his school days Sparky was awkward socially.　He was not actually disliked by the other students; no one cared that much.　He was astonished when a classmate said hello to him outside of school hours.　(2)We cannot tell how he might have done at dating.　Sparky never once asked a girl to go out in high school.　He was too afraid of being turned down.

10　However, one thing was important to Sparky——drawing.　(3)He was proud of his artwork. Of course, no one else appreciated it.　In his senior year of high school, he offered some cartoons to the editors of the *yearbook.　The cartoons were turned down.　In spite of this rejection, Sparky was so convinced of his ability that he decided to become a professional artist.

15　After finishing high school, Sparky wrote a letter to Walt Disney Studios.　He was told to send some samples of his artwork, and the subject for a cartoon was suggested.　Sparky drew the proposed cartoon.　He spent a great deal of time on it and all the other drawings.　Finally, the reply came from Walt Disney Studios.　He had been rejected (4)once again.

　So Sparky decided to write his own autobiography in cartoons.　He described his childhood

20　self——(5)a little boy loser and an all-time failure.　The cartoon character would later become famous worldwide.　Sparky, who had had such lack of success in school and whose work was rejected again and again, was Charles Schulz.　He created the "Peanuts" series and the little cartoon character whose kite would never fly and who never succeeded in kicking a football ——Charlie Brown.

(340 words)

---

²Latin[lǽt(ə)n]：ラテン語(古代ローマ帝国の言語で、中世ヨーロッパの公用語。現代では死語)
⁵consolation match：敗者復活戦　　¹²yearbook[jíərbùk]：卒業記念アルバム

CAN-DO List ☐ 〈知識・技能〉関係代名詞の非制限用法について理解できる。
☐ 〈思考力・判断力・表現力〉漫画家スパーキーについて的確に理解できる。

1. この英文全体の主旨を表すものとして最も適当なものを、次の a.～ d.から選びなさい。　（5点）

   a．自分の才能が開花するまでじっと待ち続けることが大切である。

   b．自分の才能を信じ、夢をあきらめないことが大切である。

   c．成功するためには失敗を恐れてはいけない。

   d．自分の才能を過信してはいけない。

精 読問題 もう一度英文を読んで、次の問いに答えなさい。

2. 下線部(1)の具体的な内容を、日本語で簡潔に説明しなさい。　（6点）

_____

3. 下線部(2)の理由を、日本語で説明しなさい。　（7点）

_____

4. 下線部(3)とほぼ同じ内容を表している箇所を、本文中から抜き出しなさい。　（5点）

_____

5. 下線部(4)に once again とあるのはなぜですか。日本語で説明しなさい。　（7点）

_____

6. **文法** 下線部(5)の具体的な内容を、日本語で説明しなさい。　（7点）

_____

7. **全体把握** 次の各文の ▢ に入れるのに最も適当なものを、それぞれ下の a.～ d.のうちから一つずつ選びなさい。　（各3点）

  (ア) ▢ used to be called Sparky in his school days.

    a．Charlie Brown

    b．Charles Schulz

    c．Peanuts

    d．Walt Disney

  (イ) Sparky ▢ he was rejected time after time.

    a．became very angry since

    b．lost confidence and hope because

    c．made fun of Walt Disney Studios as

    d．never gave up drawing cartoons though

  (ウ) Sparky tried to tell about himself in cartoons and he ▢ .

    a．changed his name to Charles Schulz

    b．did not succeed in kicking a football

    c．invented a world-famous character

    d．started to call himself Charlie Brown

Grammar 目標➡ 7分

1 次の各文がほぼ同じ意味になるように、（　　）内に適語を補いなさい。 (各2点)

1. We don't have a helicopter, so we cannot go there quickly.

   If we had a helicopter, we (　　　　　　　) (　　　　　　　　　) there quickly.

2. The wood is very wet, so it doesn't catch fire easily.

   If the wood (　　　　　　　) (　　　　　　　　) so wet, it would catch fire more easily.

3. The weather was very bad, so we couldn't go out.

   If the weather (　　　　　　) (　　　　　　　) so bad, we could have gone out.

4. The accident happened because the driver in front stopped so suddenly.

   The accident (　　　　　　) (　　　　　　) (　　　　　　　) if the driver in front hadn't stopped so suddenly.

2 次の各文の（　　）内の動詞を適当な形にしなさい。 (各4点)

1. I don't have enough money, but if I (have), I would buy that dress.

   _____

2. What would you do if you (find) a snake in your bathtub? _____

3. I had no map, so I got lost.　If I (have) a map, I would have been all right.

   _____

4. If I had known about the accident, I (will go) to see her in the hospital.

   _____

Writing 目標➡ 3分

3 （　　）内に与えられた語句を並べかえて、英文を完成しなさい。 (各5点)

1. エイミーはきっとお金を貸してくれるわよ。断るようなことはけっしてないわ。

   I'm sure Amy will lend you the money.　I would be (if / refused / she / surprised / very).

   _____

2. 「旅行はどうでしたか。」「まあまあでしたが、天気に恵まれていたらもっとよかったのですがね。」

   "How was your trip?"　"It was OK, but it would have been better (been / if / had / nicer / the weather)."

   _____

3. ジョンは電車に間に合って駅に着いた。乗り遅れていたら、面接に遅れていたでしょう。

   John got to the station in time to catch his train.　If he had missed it, (been / for / have / he / late / would) his interview.

   _____

CAN-DO List □ 🔍 〈知識・技能〉仮定法過去・仮定法過去完了を適切に活用することができる。

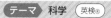
4 英文と質問を聞き、その答えとして最も適当なものを一つずつ選びなさい。 （各5点）

1. ① Blue
   ② Purple
   ③ Yellow
   ④ Red

2. ① Candlelight.
   ② Electric light.
   ③ Dinner in a restaurant.
   ④ Reading in a living room.

Rapid Reading 目標➡5分 テーマ 自然 英検®

5 （1）・（2）に入れるのに最も適当なものを一つずつ選びなさい。 （各5点）

　All the Earth's heat and light come from the sun.　Sunlight travels at 300,000 kilometers per second and （　1　） to go from the sun to the Earth.

　When sunlight shines through rain, it breaks into lots of different colors and （　2　）.　You must stand with your back to the sun with rain in front of you to see a rainbow.　The world's longest-lasting rainbow was in north Wales in Britain ――it lasted for three hours.

1. ① finds it difficult
   ② makes people refreshed
   ③ stops shining
   ④ takes about eight and a half minutes

2. ① disappears completely
   ② makes a rainbow
   ③ raises the temperature of the Earth's surface
   ④ stops traveling

Reading 目標➡20分 　文法項目 仮定法過去　テーマ 自然　◀)) 34

速読問題 次の英文を2.5分で読んで、1. の問いに答えなさい。

Where do all the colors of the rainbow come from? People have wondered about that ever since the world began. When there are things people don't understand, many stories are invented to explain them. (1)So it has been with rainbows, too.

(2)The ancient Greeks thought rainbows were special signs put in the sky by the gods to tell

5 people when terrible wars or storms would happen. Some Greeks believed a rainbow was a bridge built so that the gods could walk easily from the sky down to Earth and back again.

(3)One story is still told today——that if a person could travel to the end of a rainbow, he would find a pot of gold waiting for him there. Of course, there is no pot of gold there. There isn't even any end to some rainbows! If you fly high in an airplane, you might look

10 down and see a rainbow as a circle.

What is a rainbow, really? A rainbow is colored light. We usually see a rainbow after a storm——when the sun has come out to shine again but there is still a little rain in the air. All the colors of the rainbow are found mixed together in sunlight. When sunlight passes through raindrops, the sunlight is broken up into its different colors——(4)all the colors of the

15 rainbow! Rainbows are always in the part of the sky that is away from the sun, (5)so the only way to see a rainbow is to stand with the sun behind you. Most rainbows appear in the early morning or late afternoon, when the sun isn't too high.

However, you don't have to wait for rain to see a little rainbow. You might see one in the spray of a fountain or in a waterfall. You can even make your own rainbow. Turn on a

20 garden hose just enough to send a spray of water.

(318 words)

50 ｜ **CAN-DO List** ☐ 〈知識・技能〉仮定法過去について理解できる。
☐ 〈思考力・判断力・表現力〉虹の説明について的確に理解できる。

1. この英文のタイトルとして最も適当なものを、次のa.～d.から選びなさい。　　　　（5点）

   a．虹に関するさまざまな謎　　　　　　　　b．虹にまつわる言い伝え

   c．虹の正体　　　　　　　　　　　　　　　d．虹の作り方

精 読問題 もう一度英文を読んで、次の問いに答えなさい。

2. 下線部(1)の具体的な内容を、日本語で説明しなさい。　　　　　　　　　　　　　（6点）

_____

3. 下線部(2)の古代ギリシア人は虹をどのように説明していましたか。二つの説を日本語で述べなさい。　　　　　　　　　　　　　　　　　　　　　　　　　　　　　　　　　　（各3点）

_____

_____

4. 文法 下線部(3)の具体的な内容を、日本語で説明しなさい。　　　　　　　　　　（6点）

_____

5. 下線部(4)の生じる過程を日本語で説明しなさい。　　　　　　　　　　　　　　　（6点）

_____

6. 下線部(5)の内容と合っているものを、次のa.～c.から一つ選びなさい。　　　　（5点）

a. 　　b. 　　c.

7. 全体把握 本文の内容と合っているものにはT、合っていないものにはFと答えなさい。 （各1点）

   (ア) People have always wondered where the world came from.　　　　　（　　　　）

   (イ) People have made up many stories to explain natural events.　　　　（　　　　）

   (ウ) A person can travel to the end of a rainbow.　　　　　　　　　　　（　　　　）

   (エ) A rainbow is a circle when it is formed high up in the sky.　　　　　（　　　　）

   (オ) A rainbow is an arch of colors into which sunlight is separated.　　　（　　　　）

   (カ) You can see a rainbow between you and the sun.　　　　　　　　　（　　　　）

   (キ) You can see a small rainbow in the spray of your garden hose.　　　（　　　　）

Lesson 13 仮定法②

Grammar 目標➡ 7分

1 次の各文を I wish ＋仮定法の文に書きかえなさい。 (各4点)

1. I'm sorry I don't have a good memory.

   I wish _____.

2. It's a pity that Amanda isn't here.

   I wish _____.

3. I'm sorry I didn't learn to play a musical instrument.

   I wish _____.

2 ( )内に適語を補って、英文を完成しなさい。 (各2点)

1. 私はジェーンが嫌いです。何でも知っているかのような口ぶりをするのです。

   I don't like Jane. She talks ( ) ( ) she knew everything.

2. じゃまが入ったが、話し手は何事もなかったかのように話し続けた。

   After the interruption, the speaker went on talking as if nothing ( )
   ( ).

3. もしも太陽がなければ、生き物は生きていけない。

   If it ( ) ( ) for the sun, no creature could live.

4. あなたの援助がなかったら、私はその仕事を終えることができなかったでしょう。

   If it ( ) not ( ) for your help, I could not have finished the
   work.

Writing 目標➡ 3分

3 ( )内に与えられた語句を並べかえて、英文を完成しなさい。 (各4点)

1. 彼女の病気が重いことにもっと早く気づいていたらなあ。

   I wish I (earlier / had / how / ill / realized) she was.

   _____

2. ブライアンの運転は、まるで道路上に自分の車しかいないかのようだ。

   Brian drives as if (he / on / the only driver / the road / were).

   _____

3. かわいそうに犬たちはもう何週間も何も食べていないかのようだった。

   The poor dogs looked as if they (for / food / had / had / no) weeks.

   _____

4. あなたが注意してくれていなかったら、私は車を衝突させていたでしょう。

   I'd have crashed the car if it had (been / for / not / warning / your).

   _____

CAN-DO List □ 🔍 〈知識・技能〉願望を表す仮定法、仮定法を使った慣用表現を適切に活用することができる。

4 あなたは、授業で配られたワークシートのグラフを完成させようとしています。先生の説明を聞き、4つの空欄に入れるのに最も適当なものを一つずつ選びなさい。 (各2点)

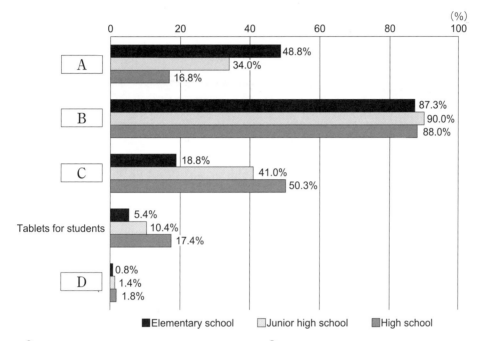

Level of Use of ICT Devices at Schools

① Tablets for teachers   ② Electric blackboards
③ PCs   ④ Video conference systems

5 (1)・(2)に入れるのに最も適当なものを一つずつ選びなさい。 (各5点)

Despite huge changes in lifestyle and technology, if you look at a classroom today and compare it to one in the early 20th century, (1). Sure, desks are more streamlined and there may be an interactive whiteboard or several computers in the room, but the basic setup is still the same —— students sit in neatly aligned desks for the majority of the day while a teacher lectures at the front of the room. Fortunately, many professionals are trying to create classroom design for the 21st century in a manner out of (2).

1. ① you'll be interested in education
   ② you'll find nothing wrong
   ③ you'll notice many significant differences
   ④ you won't notice many significant differences
2. ① the correct style
   ② the new style
   ③ the outstanding style
   ④ the traditional style

速読問題 次の英文を 3 分で読んで、1. の問いに答えなさい。

Education should be given equally to all children.　Therefore, (1)in many countries, there is a national curriculum that schools need to follow, so what children learn is already decided.　For example, all children learn *multiplication in math more or less at the same age at school.　Moreover, there are common timetables through the year which tell children when to go to school and which subjects they learn on a particular day of the week.　However, (2)some parents wonder whether all children have to attend school the same way using the same curriculum.　This is because different children learn differently.　They have their own learning style and learning pace.

It is extremely difficult for teachers to teach children according to their learning styles.　This is because in order to (3)do so, they would have to teach students individually using separate materials.　However, (4)technology offers teachers a wide choice of how they can teach.　To begin with, AI, artificial intelligence, can tell teachers the most suitable level and speed for each child.　Moreover, online video classes allow children to take lessons separately with a computer and a headset, anywhere and anytime.　Furthermore, VR, virtual reality, can make children feel as if they were experiencing activities themselves.　5G, fifth-generation mobile network, can connect these online devices quickly and stably.　For example, children can talk with peers and teachers from their homes as if they were in the same room.

The role of schools and teachers has changed dramatically since *the fourth industrial revolution.　Now AI systems control "*big data."　They can find the best study curriculum for each student from a huge store of data.　Thus, (5)adaptive learning software has been developed.　The software can work differently for each student by adjusting questions according to their level of understanding.

In this way, teaching can be adapted to learners, rather than learners trying to adapt themselves to the traditional teaching style.　It is time educators thought about what "equal education" means to individual children.

(328 words)

---

3 multiplication[mʌ̀ltɪplɪkéɪʃ(ə)n]：かけ算
17 the fourth industrial revolution：第 4 次産業革命(IoT およびビッグ・データ、また AI による技術革新)
18 big data：ICT の進展により生成・収集・蓄積等が可能・容易になった多種多量のデータの総体

CAN-DO List 　□ 〈知識・技能〉仮定法を使った慣用表現について理解できる。
　□ 〈思考力・判断力・表現力〉教育のあり方について的確に理解できる。

1. この英文のタイトルとして最も適当なものを、次の a.～ d.から選びなさい。　　　　（5点）

    a．AI Can Change the World

    b．Equal Education Is Important

    c．New Technology Changes Education

    d．VR Has Something to Do with Education

精 読問題 もう一度英文を読んで、次の問いに答えなさい。

2．下線部(1)の理由を、日本語で説明しなさい。　　　　　　　　　　　　　　　（7点）

3．下線部(2)の理由を、日本語で説明しなさい。　　　　　　　　　　　　　　　（7点）

4．下線部(3)の具体的な内容を、日本語で説明しなさい。　　　　　　　　　　　（7点）

5． 文法 下線部(4)について、AI、オンライン動画授業、VR の３つの要素が果たす役割について、それぞれ日本語でまとめなさい。　　　　　　　　　　　　　　　　　　　　　　　（各2点）

    AI：個々の子どもたちにとって（　　　　　　　　　　　　　　）を教師に教えて

    くれる。

    オンライン動画授業：（　　　　　　　　　　　　　　）があれば、子どもたちはい

    つでもどこでも個別に授業を受けることができる。

    VR：子どもたち自身が（　　　　　　　　　　　　　　）かのように感じさせるこ

    とができる。

6．下線部(5)について、次の問いに対する答えとして最も適当なものを、 a.～ d.から一つ選びなさい。

How is adaptive learning software useful for children?　　　　　　　　　　（4点）

    a．Children should adapt themselves to the traditional teaching style.

    b．The system can change questions according to each student's level.

    c．AI systems get all their data from all the children in the world.

    d．All children will need computer systems to learn anything.

7． 全体把握 本文の内容と合っているものには T、合っていないものには F と答えなさい。（各2点）

    (ア) In a national curriculum, all children learn multiplication more or less at the same age at school.　　　（　　　）

    (イ) Thanks to VR, children can feel as if they were experiencing activities.　　　（　　　）

    (ウ) 5G can connect online devices without much time lag.　　　（　　　）

    (エ) Now AI systems can find the best study curriculum for students to learn together in the same classroom.　　　（　　　）

    (オ) By using adaptive learning software, learners can adapt themselves to the traditional teaching style.　　　（　　　）

Lesson 14 名詞・冠詞・代名詞

Grammar 目標➡ 7分

1 次の各文の( )内に下記の語(句)群から適当なものを選んで補いなさい。　　(各2点)

1. Jimmy has a puppy.　Can I have ( ) too?
2. These cups are dirty.　Can we have some clean ( )?
3. Look, your glass is cracked.　I'll get you ( ).
4. Mary swam from one side of the river to ( ).
5. Some people like the ocean; ( ) like the mountains.
6. I can't do question 4 and 5, but I've done all ( ).

　　【another / one / ones / others / the other / the others】

2 次の各文の( )内に入れるのに最も適当なものを選んで補いなさい。　　(各2点)

1. You can have ( ) chicken or fish, but I would recommend the chicken.
　　【both / either / neither】
2. The climate here is milder than ( ) of Scotland.
　　【one / this / that】
3. ( ) of my friends has his or her own dream.
　　【All / Each / Every】
4. ( ) children like to play.
　　【Almost / Most / Most of】
5. The children were so tired that they found ( ) difficult to keep awake.
　　【it / this / that】

Writing 目標➡ 3分

3 ( )内に与えられた語句を並べかえて、英文を完成しなさい。　　(各4点)

1. 彼女は赤ちゃんを片腕に、洗濯物の山をもう一方の腕に抱えていた。
　　She was holding the baby in one arm and (a pile / in / of / the other / washing).

　　_____

2. 謝るか出て行くか、どちらかにしろ。
　　(either / or / sorry / say / you're) get out!

　　_____

3. 私には休暇をとる暇もお金もありません。
　　I have (neither / nor the money / the time / to) go on vacation.

　　_____

4. 人々はもはや、男性が髪を長くしているのを奇妙だとはみなしていません。
　　People no longer consider it (for / let / men / strange / to) their hair grow long.

　　_____

4 長めの対話を一つ聞き、問いの答えとして最も適当なものを一つずつ選びなさい。 （各5点）

1. What does Kana recommend that Geena should do?
   ① Buy stamps at the school shop.
   ② Put her letter into a post box.
   ③ Send her music player by regular mail.
   ④ Send her music player by registered mail.

2. What will Geena probably do next?
   ① She'll go up to the second floor.　② She'll look for a post box.
   ③ She'll go toward the station.　④ She'll go to Nagoya.

Rapid Reading 目標➡5分 テーマ 道案内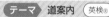

5 Eメールを読み取って、問いに対する答えとして最も適当なものを一つずつ選びなさい。（各5点）

To: Prof. Kent	From: John and Elizabeth
Date: April 10	Subject: Wedding Reception

Dear Prof. Kent,

We got legally married in March.　We are going to hold a wedding reception at the Castle Hotel on July 6. We'd like you to attend it and make a speech.　It is easy to get there by tram.　Just follow these directions: First, take the Green Line from Central bound for Green Park and go three stations to City Center.　Then transfer to the Blue Line bound for South Station.　Get off at Castle Street, which is the second station.　Go to the right in front of the station and walk along Castle Street for a few minutes until you come to the Castle Hotel on the right.　We'll meet there at 11:00 a.m.　We're looking forward to seeing you.

Sincerely,

John and Elizabeth

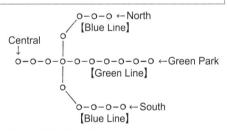

1. Which station is between Central Station and Castle Street Station?
   ① North Station.　② Green Park Station.
   ③ City Center Station.　④ South Station.

2. Which of the following statements is true?
   ① It's difficult to get to the Castle Hotel.
   ② It's necessary to transfer the tram to get to the Castle Hotel from the Central Station.
   ③ There is the Castle Hotel in front of the Castle Street Station.
   ④ It is far from the Castle Street Station to the Castle Hotel.

Reading   目標➡20分   文法項目 いろいろな代名詞   テーマ 道案内   🔊 38

速 読問題 次の英文を2.5分で読んで、1. の問いに答えなさい。

I have a special rule for travel: never carry a map. I prefer to ask for (1)directions. Sometimes I get lost, but I usually have a good time.   I can practice a new language, meet new people, learn new customs.   And I can find out about different "styles" of directions every time I ask, "How can I get to the post office?"

5   (2)Foreign tourists are often confused in Japan.   That's because most streets there don't have names; in Japan, people often use landmarks in their directions instead of street names. For example, the Japanese might tell travelers something like this: "Go straight down to the corner.   Turn left at the big hotel with the sushi bar and go past a fruit market.   The post office is across from the bus stop."

10   In the countryside of the American Midwest, there are not usually many landmarks. There are no mountains, so the land is very flat; in many places there are no towns or buildings for miles.   Instead of landmarks, people will tell you (3)directions and distances.   For instance, people will say, "Go straight north two miles.   Turn east, and then go another mile."

  On the other hand, people in Los Angeles, California, (4)have no idea of distance in miles;
15 they measure distance in time, not miles.   "How far away is the post office?" you ask.   "Oh," they answer, "I guess it's about five minutes from here."   You say, "Yes, but how many miles away is it——or how many kilometers or blocks?"   They don't know.

  Sometimes a person doesn't know the answer to your question.   What happens in (5)this situation?   A New Yorker might say, "Sorry, I have no idea."   (6)But in *Yucatan, Mexico, no
20 one answers, "I don't know."   People in Yucatan believe it impolite to say, "I don't know"; they stay and talk to you, and usually they'll try to give you an answer, even if it is a wrong one.

(322 words)

---

19 Yucatan [jùːkətǽn]：ユカタン半島(メキシコの南東部にある)

CAN-DO List   ☐ 🔍 〈知識・技能〉いろいろな代名詞について理解できる。
☐ 🏆 〈思考力・判断力・表現力〉道案内のし方について的確に理解できる。

1. この英文で述べられているものを、次のa.～d.から選びなさい。　　　　　　　（5点）

   a. 地域によって異なる会話の楽しみ方

   b. 地域によって異なる外国人への対応のし方

   c. 地域によって異なる道案内のし方

   d. 地域によって異なる郵便局の位置

精 読問題 もう一度英文を読んで、次の問いに答えなさい。

2. 下線部(1)、(3)のdirectionsの意味を、それぞれ簡単な日本語で答えなさい。　　（各3点）

   (1) _____　　(3) _____

3. 下線部(2)の理由を、日本語で説明しなさい。　　　　　　　　　　　　　　（6点）

   _____

4. 下線部(4)の具体的な内容を、日本語で説明しなさい。　　　　　　　　　　（5点）

   _____

5. 下線部(5)の具体的な内容を、日本語で説明しなさい。　　　　　　　　　　（5点）

   _____

6. 文法 下線部(6)の理由とその結果生じる状況を、日本語で簡単に説明しなさい。　（各3点）

   理由：_____

   結果：_____

7. 全体把握 次の各文の _____ に入れるのに最も適当なものを、それぞれ下のa.～d.のうちから一つずつ選びなさい。　　　　　　　　　　　　　　　　　　　　　　　　　　　（各3点）

   (ア) Japanese people tend to _____ as a guide to a place.

   　　a. list the names of the streets

   　　b. use directions and distances

   　　c. draw a map of the town

   　　d. refer to noticeable things such as a high building

   (イ) _____ , when giving directions, people usually tell how long it takes.

   　　a. In Japan　　　　　　　　　　　　b. In the American Midwest

   　　c. In Los Angeles, California　　　　d. In New York

   (ウ) In Yucatan, Mexico, _____ .

   　　a. information people give about the way is sometimes incorrect

   　　b. official guides tell us the way quickly

   　　c. most people have a good sense of direction

   　　d. people don't have the habit of reading maps

Lesson 15 形容詞・副詞

Grammar 目標➡ 7分

1 次の各文の（　）内に下記の語（句）群から適当なものを選んで補いなさい。 （各2点）

1. I have (　　　　　　　) friends, so I'm not lonely.
2. I can't decide now──I need (　　　　　　　) time to think about it.
3. There were (　　　　　　　) jobs in the town, and many families lived in poverty.
4. There was (　　　　　　　) food in the fridge.　It was almost empty.
   【a few / very few / a little / very little】

2 次の各文の（　）内に入れるのに最も適当なものを選んで補いなさい。 （各2点）

1. It is always (　　　　　　　) to hear other people's point of view.
   【interest / interested / interesting】
2. How can you be so (　　　　　　　) about a stupid computer game？
   【excite / excited / exciting】
3. It's getting very dark.　I can (　　　　　　　) see the ship anymore.
   【almost / hardly / nearly】
4. I (　　　　　　　) go to the movies；I go only two to three times a year.
   【never / often / seldom】
5. Well done, Robert, your sums are (　　　　　　　) from mistakes today！
   【away / far / free】

Writing 目標➡ 3分

3 （　）内に与えられた語句を並べかえて、英文を完成しなさい。 （各4点）

1. 今日の新聞にはおもしろいものは何も載っていない。
   There (anything / interesting / in / isn't / the newspaper) today.

   _____

2. 今日、車を修理工場へもって行きます。ブレーキの調子が悪いのです。
   I'm taking my car to the garage today ── (something / the brakes / there's / with / wrong).

   _____

3. 私からもう一度お金を借りようと思ったって、まずだめだよ。
   You can (expect / hardly / lend / me / to) you money again.

   _____

4. ネコはとてもきれい好きな動物で、体や周囲の環境を汚さないようにすると考えられています。
   Cats are supposed to be very clean animals and keep (and their surroundings / free / from / dirt / themselves).

   _____

CAN-DO List □ 〈知識・技能〉数量を示す形容詞、形容詞と同じ分詞・否定語を含まない否定表現・準否定語を適切に活用することができる。

Listening

目標➡ 5分　　　　　　　　　　　　テーマ フードマイル　🔊 39

4 長めの英文を一つ聞き、問いの答えとして最も適当なものを一つずつ選びなさい。 （各5点）

1. According to the speaker, what is imported from Australia?

① Beef and soybeans.　　　② Beef and corn.

③ Soybeans.　　　　　　　④ Beef.

2. What does the speaker want to tell us most?

① What is needed to import foods.

② That we cannot live without imported foods.

③ That imported foods are not always good.

④ That cheap foods are good for the environment.

Rapid Reading

目標➡ 5分　　　　　　　　　　　　テーマ フードマイル

5 グラフを読み取って、問いに対する答えとして最も適当なものを一つずつ選びなさい。 （各5点）

The Annual *Food Mileage of Imported Products

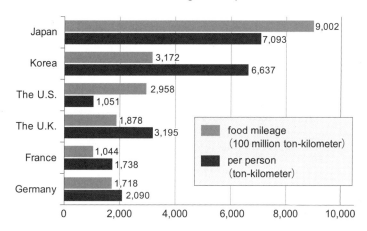

*Food Mileage：フードマイレージ（食料輸入量に輸出入国間の距離をかけた数値、単位はトン・キロメートル）

1. Which country has the least food mileage per person?

① Korea　　　　② The U.S.　　　　③ France　　　　④ Germany

2. Which of the following statements is best supported by the above graph?

① Japan imports lots of agricultural products.

② The U.S. is exposed to pollution.

③ France isn't an agricultural state.

④ The trend in the food mileages between the West and the East is almost the same.

Reading　目標➡20分　　　文法項目　副詞　テーマ　社会問題　🔊 40

速読問題 次の英文を３分で読んで、1. の問いに答えなさい。

(1)What are food miles?　Put simply, food miles are the measure of the distance a food travels from field to plate.　Agriculture and food now account for nearly 30 per cent of goods transported on our roads.　This travel adds substantially to the carbon dioxide that is contributing to climate change——which is why food miles matter.　A new report by *the Department for the Environment, Food and Rural Affairs says that food miles rose by 15 per cent between 1992 and 2002.

Food travels further these days partly because the centralized systems of supermarkets have taken over from local and regional markets.　(2)It is hard to believe, but a *pint of milk or a crop of potatoes can be transported many miles to be packaged at a central location and then sent many miles back to be sold near where they were produced in the first place.　Also, because of the way the food processing industry works, ingredients travel around the country from factory to factory, before they make their way to the shops.

Then there's imported produce.　Ninety-five per cent of the fruit and half of the vegetables in the UK are imported.　The amount of food being flown into the UK doubled in the 1990s and is predicted to rise (3)further each year.　To take one example, strawberries are flown in from warmer climates to satisfy our desire for (4)all-season summer foods, and air freight has a far bigger impact on the environment than sea or road travel has.　Another reason for mounting food miles is comparative labor costs.　For example, some British fish is now sent to China where labor costs are much lower for processing, then sent back to the UK to be sold.

(5)Consumers are also directly responsible for increased food miles.　We now travel further for our shopping and use the car more often to do it.　Each year, the average UK adult travels about 135 miles by car to shop for food, *more often than not making trips to large, out-of-town supermarkets.　This is something we consumers should think about carefully when deciding where we will do our grocery shopping.

(358 words)

---

⁴the Department for the Environment, Food and Rural Affairs：環境食糧省
⁸pint[páint]：パイント（容量単位、約0.5*l*)　　²²more often than not：通常、たいてい

CAN-DO List　☐ 🖊 〈知識・技能〉副詞について理解できる。
　　　　　　　☐ 🖊 〈思考力・判断力・表現力〉フードマイルについて的確に理解できる。

1. この英文で主に述べられているものを、次のa.～d.から選びなさい。　　　　　　　　（5点）

   a. フードマイルとは何か　　　　　　　　b. フードマイル拡大のもたらすもの

   c. フードマイル拡大の諸原因　　　　　　d. フードマイル拡大の抑制

精 読問題 もう一度英文を読んで、次の問いに答えなさい。

2. 下線部(1)の food miles について、日本語で簡潔に説明しなさい。　　　　　　　（7点）

3. 下線部(2)の It の指すものを、日本語で説明しなさい。　　　　　　　　　　　（8点）

4. 文法 下線部(3)の further とほぼ同じ意味の further を含む文をa.～d.から一つ選びなさい。

                                      （3点）

   a. Can I have time to consider the matter <u>further</u>?

   b. He's too tired to walk any <u>further</u>.

   c. I can remember any <u>further</u> back than 1970.

   d. The house is not large enough for us, and <u>further</u>, it is too far from the town.

5. 下線部(4)の具体的な内容を、日本語で説明しなさい。　　　　　　　　　　　（7点）

6. 下線部(5)の具体的な内容を、日本語で簡単に説明しなさい。　　　　　　　　（7点）

7. 全体把握 次の各文の ____ に入れるのに最も適当なものを、それぞれ下のa.～d.のうちから一つずつ選びなさい。　　　　　　　　　　　　　　　　　　　　　　　　　　　　（各3点）

  (ア) Food miles show the distance that food has traveled before it reaches ____ .

     a. a large, out-of-town supermarket　　　b. local markets

     c. the consumer　　　　　　　　　　　　d. the producer

  (イ) When produce is carried by truck, ship, or plane, ____ .

     a. a large amount of CO_2 is emitted

     b. a lot of people support themselves with the transportation work

     c. the additional cost of transportation is included in its price

     d. the labor costs are brought down

  (ウ) More food miles mean ____ .

     a. a bigger impact on the environment

     b. a higher price of the produce

     c. a more international dinner table

     d. the better local economy

Sources

■Listening

Lesson 13（グラフ）
　英語教育実施状況調査（文部科学省）をもとに作成

■Rapid Reading

Lesson 12
　Extract from："American Shine 2 Student Book"
　©P. Prowse；J. Garton-Sprenger 2002, Published by Macmillan Publishers Limited.　Used by Permission.3
　All Rights Reserved

Lesson 15（グラフ）
　日本の輸入食料のフード・マイレージの変化とその背景（農林水産省統計部）をもとに作成

■Reading

Lesson 5
　The Asahi Shimbun Asia & Japan Watch（AJW）, January 10, 2020

Lesson 13
　産業能率大学　2021年度入学試験問題（一部改変）